INDUSTRIAL LASERS AND THEIR APPLICATIONS

INDUSTRIAL LASERS
AND THEIR APPLICATIONS

JOHN E. HARRY

Electricity Council Senior Lecturer in Electroheat
University of Technology Loughborough, Leicestershire, England.

London · New York · St Louis · San Francisco · Auckland · Düsseldorf
Johannesburg · Kuala Lumpur · Mexico · Montreal · New Delhi · Panama · Paris
São Paulo · Singapore · Sydney · Tokyo · Toronto

Published by

McGraw-Hill Book Company (UK) Limited

MAIDENHEAD · BERKSHIRE · ENGLAND

Library of Congress Cataloging in Publication Data

Harry, John E., Date
  Industrial lasers and their applications.

  Includes bibliographical references.
  1. Lasers.   I. Title.
TA1675.H37   621.36′6   74–8197
ISBN 0–07–084443–7

Printed in Great Britain by Hazell Watson & Viney Ltd, Aylesbury, Bucks

To my wife and family

CONTENTS

Preface   ix
Notation   xi

CHAPTER 1. INTRODUCTION TO OPTICAL RADIATION PROCESSES   1
1.1   Emission Processes   1
1.2   Fluorescence   5
1.3   Stimulated Emission   6
1.4   The Operation of a Laser   8
References   10

CHAPTER 2. LASER CHARACTERISTICS   11
2.1   Output Wavelength   11
2.2   Divergence   13
2.3   Mode Structure   16
2.4   Coherence   17
2.5   Polarization   18
2.6   Energy and Power Output   20
2.7   Energy Transfer and Efficiency   22
References   23

CHAPTER 3. MATERIALS AND COMPONENTS USED IN LASER
            SYSTEMS   24
3.1   Optical Properties of Materials   24
3.2   Bi-Refringent Materials   36
3.3   Reflectors   47
3.4   Lenses   52
3.5   Light Guides   58
3.6   Q Switches   59
3.7   Wavelength Selection   60
3.8   Spatial Filters   62
3.9   Optical Attenuators   62
3.10 Detectors and Calorimeters   62
3.11 Scanning Methods   65
References   65

CHAPTER 4. INDUSTRIAL LASERS   68
4.1   Solid-state Lasers   71
4.2   Pumping Sources for Solid-state Lasers   73
4.3   Solid-state Laser Materials   77
4.4   Gas Lasers   81
4.5   The Principal Gas Lasers   83
4.6   Dye Lasers   87
4.7   Semiconductor Lasers   89
4.8   Other Lasers   92
References   93

CHAPTER 5. INDUSTRIAL LASER APPLICATIONS   96
5.1   The Use of Lasers in Metrology   96
5.2   Laser Fabrication Processes   112
5.3   Application of Lasers in the Manufacture of Electronic Components   135
5.4   Medical Applications   140
5.5   Inspection Techniques and Non-Destructive Testing Using Lasers   145
5.6   Pollution Detection   147
5.7   Analytical Techniques Using Lasers   148
5.8   Applications of Holography   151
5.9   Communications and Information Processing   155
5.10 Other Applications   156
References   160

CHAPTER 6. SAFETY   167
6.1   Transmission and Absorption of the Eye   167
6.2   Effect on the Body   171
6.3   Threshold Levels   172
6.4   Eye Protection   175
6.5   Precautionary Measures   175
References   179

Selected Reading List   180
Appendix 1   Sources of Information   182
Appendix 2   Glossary   183

Index   186

PREFACE

This book is concerned primarily with the application of lasers in industry. It is written for the engineer who does not require a specialized knowledge of lasers but is concerned with how their application may affect his own area of interest in industry. The book assumes no specialist knowledge of lasers or optics.

The most important chapter is chapter 5, 'Industrial laser applications' and it is perhaps to this that the inquiring reader will first turn. The preceding chapters prepare the background to enable the application of lasers to be understood in adequate depth so that the potential user can evaluate their potential application in his own situation.

In chapter 1 conventional light sources and lasers are considered. The important characteristics of lasers that influence their application are described in chapter 2. Few laser applications utilize a laser alone, the laser usually forming part of a system which may also include lenses, mirrors, detectors, modulators, and other optical components. Optical materials and devices together with factors which influence their design and application are described in chapter 3.

Many books and papers have been written on lasers from the viewpoint of laser theory and development. Chapter 4 considers the application of lasers that are commercially available.

The applications of lasers are described in chapter 5; wherever possible the principle of operation is illustrated together with the advantages and limitations of lasers compared with other methods. The emphasis is on reported applications rather than potential uses and nearly 200 different selected references from technical and trade publications covering applications as diversified as surveying, welding, fire detection, and pollution detection are included.

A book of this kind would be incomplete without a reference to safety. The effects of wavelength, power, and output (continuous or pulsed) are described in chapter 6. Precautionary measures and details of optical examinations are also given together with permissible threshold values. References are also given to the various safety codes in the United Kingdom and North America. A selected reading list is given at the end of the book as well as the references at the end of each chapter.

A list of the principal publications dealing with lasers and their applications is given in Appendix 1, and a glossary of terms which may be unfamiliar is given in Appendix 2.

An enormous amount has been published on lasers and related subjects. This book presents for the first time a selection of data from the principal areas related to laser applications and provides a unique source of reference to data in a wide number of related fields.

It is hoped that this book will result in a wider knowledge of what can be achieved with lasers as industrial tools. It is my belief that the industrial application of lasers will continue to increase together with the commercial and domestic applications already in advanced stages of development.

In conclusion, I should like to acknowledge the helpful criticism of Dr D. C. W. Morley of the Corporate Laboratory, ICI Ltd, Runcorn, and the cooperation of Mr F. W. Lunau of BOC Ltd, whose foresight led to the first major application of the CO_2 laser in industry.

J. E. Harry
April 1974

NOTATION

(i) LATIN ALPHABET

A area, m^2

A amplitude

B electro-optic constant (Kerr effect) m/V^2

c speed of light in vacuo ($3 \times 10^8\,m/s$)

C capacitance, F

d diameter, m

D optical density

e base of natural logarithm (2·718)

E energy, J

E electric field strength, V/m

E_r electro-optic coefficient, V/m

f frequency, Hz

f focal length

F aperture, d/f

h Planck's constant ($6·6 \times 10^{-34}\,J/s$)

H magnetic force, A/m

I intensity

k coefficient of absorption

l length, m

M acousto-optic figure of merit

n refractive index

p pressure, N/m^2

P power, W

R radius of curvature, m

t thickness, m

T coefficient of transmissivity

T absolute temperature, K

u object distance from principal plane, m

U velocity, m/s

v image distance from principal plane, m

V voltage, V

V' half-wave voltage, V

V Magneto-optic constant (Verdet's effect), rad $T^{-1} m^{-1}$
x distance, m
z depth of focus, m

(ii) GREEK ALPHABET

α angle of divergence, rad
β coefficient of reflectivity
γ wavenumber, m^{-1}
δ diffraction limited diameter, m
ε emissivity coefficient
ε_r relative permittivity
η efficiency
θ angle of deflection, rad
λ wavelength, m
λ_0 characteristic wavelength, m
ρ density, kg/m^3
σ Stefan–Boltzman constant ($5 \cdot 67 \times 10^{-8}\ Wm^{-2}\ K^{-4}$)
ϕ angular diameter, rad
ω diameter (measured between equal intensity points), m
ω rate of angular rotation, rad/s

1

INTRODUCTION TO OPTICAL RADIATION
PROCESSES

This chapter considers the various important characteristics of optical radiation processes and, in particular, compares the characteristics of conventional and laser light sources.

Light, like radio waves, microwaves, and heat is a form of electromagnetic energy. All electromagnetic radiation processes are essentially similar and obey the same fundamental laws although their affects vary with frequency. The electromagnetic spectrum is illustrated in Fig. 1.1 with the optical and visible spectrum shown enlarged. We are concerned here with radiation in the optical part of the spectrum which extends from the ultraviolet to the far infrared including the visible region and can be treated in terms of optical theory. (Several reference texts on physical optics are given in the selected reading list at the end of the book.)

The ultraviolet end of the spectrum is limited by the availability of suitable sources and the limited transmission of materials including air. The infrared region extends from the near infrared at the end of the visible part of the spectrum to the far infrared at millimetre wavelengths corresponding to microwave frequencies and has been very extensively investigated. The visible region is only a small part of the total optical spectrum.

Wavelengths at radio frequencies are normally expressed in metres. Wavelengths in the optical part of the spectrum are very much shorter and are expressed in SI units as micrometres (μm, 10^{-6} m) or nanometres (nm, 10^{-9} m). Another unit formerly widely used is the ångström (Å, 10^{-10} m).

1.1 Emission processes

An atom can be visualized as a central core of positive charge that is surrounded by a number of electrons as shown in Fig. 1.2. These electrons revolve around the core in a limited number of possible orbits. Other orbits between the allowed orbits are prohibited. An electron can change its orbit, resulting in a transition in energy level by emitting light when it moves towards the core and absorbing light when it moves

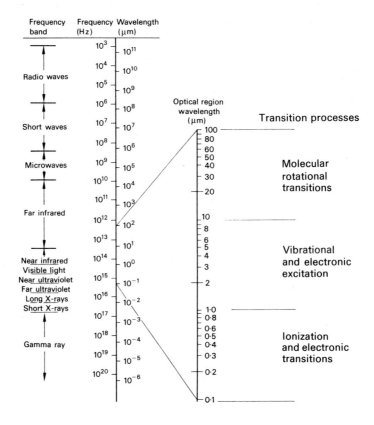

Fig. 1.1 *The electromagnetic spectrum*

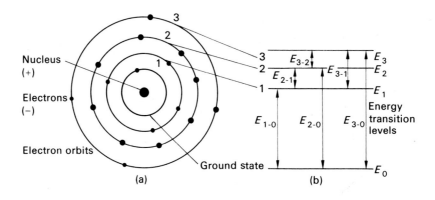

Fig. 1.2 *Relation of energy transition levels to electron orbits:* (a) *nucleus and orbiting electrons;* (b) *energy level diagram*

outwards from the core. Associated with each transition is a specific quantity of energy (quantum) and wavelength. The energy, E, associated with the transition increases as the wavelength decreases, according to the relation

$$E = hf = \frac{hc}{\lambda}$$

(1.1)

where c is the velocity of light (3×10^8 m/s in free space), λ is the wavelength in metres, f is the frequency in hertz, and h is Planck's constant ($6 \cdot 6 \times 10^{-34}$ J s).

A more detailed treatment of emission processes can be found in the books on physical and geometrical optics listed in the selected reading list at the end of the book.

1.1.1 Sources of continuous radiation Incandescent radiation sources such as tungsten filament lamps emit radiation over a wide range of wavelengths corresponding to the large number of electron transitions that occur simultaneously between different energy levels (Fig. 1.2). The energy associated with these changes in transition energy levels is absorbed and re-radiated spontaneously. This is illustrated schematically in Fig. 1.3. Energy is absorbed by the transition of an electron from an inner to an outer level, this is re-radiated spontaneously at frequencies corresponding to the change in energy level when a downward transition occurs.

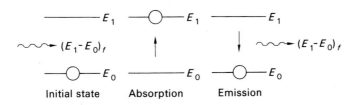

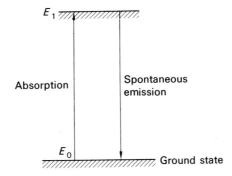

Fig. 1.3 *Spontaneous emission:* (a) *absorption and re-radiation by spontaneous emission;* (b) *energy transition diagram*

The intensity of the output varies with both temperature and wavelength. The total energy radiated is the sum of the energy radiated over the range of output wavelengths. For most thermal radiation sources the total radiated energy is approximately proportional to the fourth power of the temperature

$$W = \sigma T^4 \text{ (watts)}$$

(1.2)

where σ is the Stefan–Boltzman constant ($5{\cdot}67 \times 10^{-8}$ W m^{-2} K^{-4}). The radiated energy of a perfect emitter (black body) has been tabulated as a function of temperature and wavelength.[1] Figure 1.4 shows the variation in intensity as a function of wavelength at various temperatures. The wavelength at which the intensity of radiated output is a maximum is shown by the broken line and is given by Wien's Law

$$\lambda_{max}T = 2{\cdot}9 \times 10^{-3} \, \text{m K} \tag{1.3}$$

i.e., as the temperature increases the wavelength at which the maximum occurs becomes shorter and relatively more energy is radiated in the visible region.

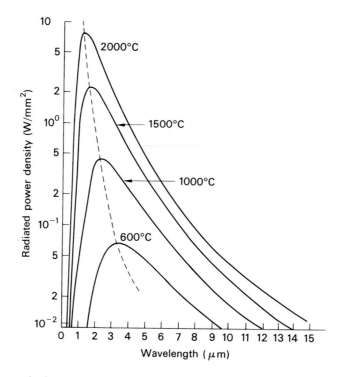

Fig. 1.4 *Variation of radiated power density of a black body with temperature and wavelength (peak intensity lies on broken line)*

The radiated power output of practical sources is normally less than that for a black body, and they are referred to as non-black bodies. An emission coefficient which varies with the material and its surface condition is used so that the equation for the radiated output becomes

$$W = \varepsilon\sigma T^4 \, \text{(watts)} \tag{1.4}$$

where ε is the coefficient of emissivity and $\varepsilon \leqslant 1$. For real bodies the emissivity also varies with wavelength. Values of mean emissivity and spectral emissivity have been tabulated.[1] The spectral intensity curve for a non-black body is illustrated in Fig. 1.5 together with the black body curve.

The maximum total intensity of radiated output and the intensity at a given wave-

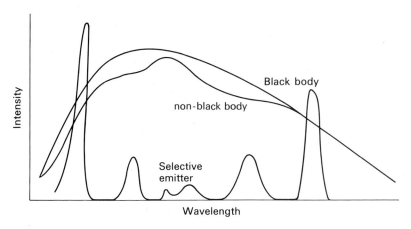

Fig. 1.5 *Variation of intensity of a black and non-black body source, a selective emitter with wavelength*

length are limited by the thermal properties of the material used. The maximum operating temperature of incandescent light sources is limited to temperatures of about 3000°C and radiated power densities of the order of 6 W/mm².

1.1.2 Selective emitters Light can also be emitted over narrow bands of wavelengths over the optical spectrum (selective emission). An example of the output of a selective emitter is also shown in Fig. 1.5. The absorption and emission process is similar to that for continuous sources of radiation but is confined to a limited number of electron transitions. These are selectively excited by an external source such as an electric field and emit light by spontaneous emission in the same way as continuous sources of radiation but over narrow bands of wavelength. Various possible atomic and inter-molecular transitions normally exist giving outputs at bands of different wavelengths. The output over a narrow band approaches that of a monochromatic source. The intensity of the output of a selective emitter is not limited by the black body curve. Some examples of selective emitters are gas discharges, fluorescent and phosphorescent materials, solid state light sources, and lasers. The output from selective emitters with the exception of lasers is usually incoherent. (See also Section 2.4.)

1.2 Fluorescence

Some materials when they are exposed to light of a given wavelength are observed to re-emit light of a different, and usually longer wavelength. This is illustrated schematically in Fig. 1.6. This phenomenon is called fluorescence, and is most often apparent when various minerals are exposed to ultraviolet light (which is invisible to the naked eye) and are observed to glow with some other visible colour at a longer wavelength. A few special materials have arrangements of electron levels that allow part of the energy to be re-radiated at shorter wavelengths.

The electron transition during fluorescence is schematically illustrated in Fig. 1.6. The only transition from the excited level E_1 to the ground level is via E_2 which results in reradiation of visible light. Some fluorescent materials possess metastable states which have unusually long lived states and enable energy to be stored at intermediate

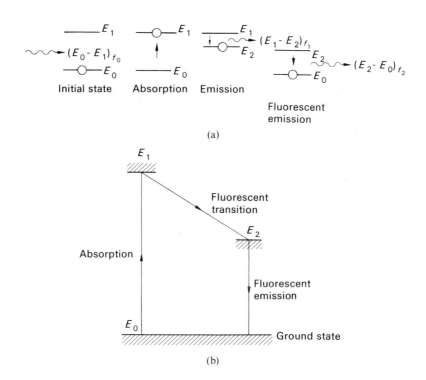

Fig. 1.6 *Fluorescence:* (a) *absorption and re-radiation by fluorescence;* (b) *energy transition diagram*

energy levels before being re-radiated so that energy at an intermediate level is built up. This is the basis of stimulated emission.

1.3 Stimulated emission

Stimulated emission is the reverse process of absorption, i.e., an induced downward transition occurs in which a photon liberates a new photon rather than being absorbed. For laser action to occur the number of electrons (population) at two levels has to be inverted from the normal (ground) state so that more than 50 per cent of the ground state is at the laser transition level. This results in the probability that a photon of the correct frequency will induce a stimulated photon is greater than that of its being absorbed.

Spontaneous emission tends to prevent sufficient change in energy levels for a population inversion to occur. For this reason population inversion often occurs between levels of which the upper is metastable, i.e., its probability of undergoing a spontaneous transition to the lower level is low. A population inversion can also occur where the lifetimes of lower levels are very short compared with those of higher energy levels, as in the argon laser.

The process of stimulated emission is shown schematically in Fig. 1.7. Energy is absorbed raising the energy level from the ground state E_0 to E_1. This decays spontaneously to E_2. A photon resulting from a transition from the fluorescent state back to E_0 (which will be at a different wavelength from the exciting radiation), stimu-

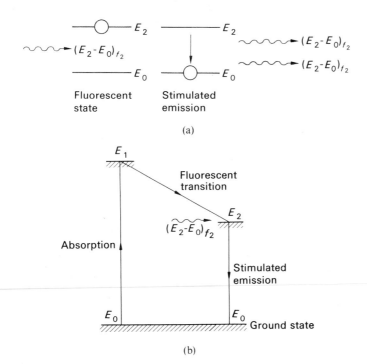

Fluorescent state

Stimulated emission

(a)

E_1

Fluorescent transition

E_2

$(E_2-E_0)_{f_2}$

Absorption

Stimulated emission

E_0

E_0 Ground state

(b)

Fig. 1.7 *Stimulated emission:* (a) *absorption and re-radiation by stimulated emission;* (b) *energy transition diagram*

lates another transition from E_2 to E_0 so that now two photons are available. The second photon has the same phase as the first photon. These in turn can liberate two more photons also with the same phase so that a rapid cumulative build-up of light output results which has the same phase as the initial triggering photon. It is this feedback action which results in the amplification obtainable and the monochromatic and coherent nature of the emission that can be obtained from a laser.

The intensity of stimulated emission is not limited by the condition of black body radiation. The high spectral intensity (intensity per unit bandwidth) results from the regenerative nature of laser amplification which causes a decrease in line-width with increase in laser power.

The properties of stimulated emission enable spatially and temporally coherent light output to be obtained (i.e., the light at different points along the beam and transverse to it bear a fixed phase relation) not possible with sources of spontaneous emission (see chapter 2).

It is these characteristics of laser radiation that result in the principal properties of interest namely:

(a) High intensity output not limited by black body radiation laws
(b) Monochromatic output
(c) High degree of spatial and temporal coherence
(d) Low divergence

although not all are necessarily obtainable from one type of laser.

7

1.4 The operation of a laser

Light Amplification by Stimulated Emission of Radiation requires the combination of population inversion, stimulated emission, and amplification. The laser process can be most simply considered in terms of a solid-state laser such as the ruby laser which was the first to be discovered. The various other types of laser are essentially similar in concept.

The active laser material is normally contained in a suitable host. For the ruby laser the active material is chromic oxide and the host is aluminium oxide. The percentage of active material (dopant) is often critical and impurities can reduce or prevent laser action.

The host material is required to be transparent to both the exciting radiation and the laser output which are often at widely separated wavelengths.

The host is normally cylindrical. Although the power output is a function of laser volume the attenuation of the pumping radiation with increase in diameter limits the maximum diameter that can be used although the length is not limited in this way.

Solid-state lasers use optical excitation (pumping) by one or more flash tubes in a reflecting cavity mounted along the axis of the laser rod. Only a small part of the total light output from the flash tube is absorbed by the fluorescent transition of the laser material. The remainder of the light is dissipated in the laser material as heat.

The energy absorbed by the fluorescent transition is stored at an intermediate level. If the pumping radiation is adequate a population inversion occurs with the result that if a photon decays from the intermediate level thereby emitting light it has a probability of inducing a second transition by the process of stimulated emission. The additional photon is characterized by the same wavelength and has the same energy and phase as the first photon, and each of these photons can in turn stimulate the emission of new photons (Fig. 1.7). For a pulsed laser the process results in an avalanche effect so that all the laser transitions occur in a very short time. Where the output is continuous the output power is less and a saturation level is reached at which the rate of decay from the laser transition levels is equal to the energy input from the pumping source.

The build-up of stimulated emission along the laser axis is shown schematically in Fig. 1.8. Initially spontaneous transitions occur. Those whose direction of radiation is along the axis of the laser have the longest path length in the laser medium and are more likely to stimulate further emission. This in turn is amplified by the mirrors at either end of the laser cavity.

In practice light from the laser transitions would be emitted in all directions from the ends of the rod and the cumulative build-up of emission would be prevented (light transmission through the cylindrical walls is usually small since the angle of incidence is normally greater than the critical angle so that total internal reflection occurs). The cumulative build-up of emission is enhanced by placing mirrors at either end of the rod. One of the mirrors is made totally reflecting, the other partially reflecting so that a proportion of the incident light is transmitted. The mirrors are aligned perpendicularly to the optic axis of the laser rod so that only light on the laser axis is reflected and transmitted resulting in the preferential build-up of light emitted along the direction of the laser axis. This results in positive feedback so that a rapid cumulative build-up of radiation along the laser axis occurs. Since many passes along the laser axis occur in a very short time (at the velocity of light) although the percentage of the incident energy

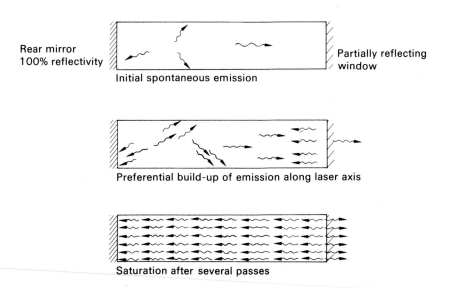

Rear mirror
100% reflectivity

Partially reflecting
window

Initial spontaneous emission

Preferential build-up of emission along laser axis

Saturation after several passes

Fig. 1.8 *Feedback and amplification of radiation on axis of laser*

transmitted by the output window may be small at each pass the total energy transmitted in even a very short time is high.

Because feedback only occurs along the axis of the laser material the light output is not radiated uniformly in all directions but is directed along the laser axis in one direction as a narrow beam of low divergence governed by the laser optics and geometry and limited by diffraction at the output window.

The laser rod and mirrors are referred to as the laser cavity. Since the effect of the amplification of a narrow wavelength is similar to the behaviour of a resonant electrical circuit it is also referred to as an oscillator, an optical resonator, or a resonating cavity. The laser rod together with mirrors, flash tubes, and reflectors which usually form an integral unit is referred to as the laser head. If no mirrors are used, it is referred to as an amplifier and this configuration is sometimes used in oscillator–amplifier configurations.

Various geometrical considerations including the radius of curvature of the mirrors and the length and diameter of the cavity determine the degree of feedback and whether laser action can occur.

The condition determining whether a geometrical ray in the cavity will be reflected in terms of the geometry of the cavity is given by

$$ 0 < \left(1 - \frac{d}{R_1}\right)\left(1 - \frac{d}{R_2}\right) < 1 $$

where d is the diameter of the cavity and R_1 and R_2 are the radii of curvature of the mirrors.

The stability conditions derived from this are shown in Fig. 1.9 with the parameters d/R_1 and d/R_2 together with the displaced co-ordinate corresponding to $(1 - d/R_1)$ and $(1 - d/R_2)$. The various resonator types are indicated on the diagram according to their corresponding stability. Unstable configurations are shown in the shaded areas.

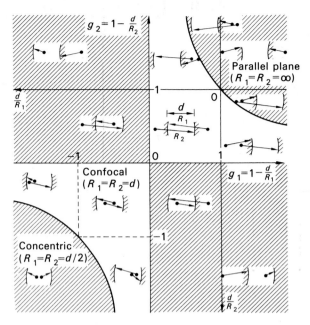

Fig. 1.9 *Stability diagram. Unstable resonator systems lie in shaded regions (from Kogelnik, H. and Li, T., 'Laser Beams and Resonators', Appl. Opt., 5 (10), 1550–1567, 1966. © Optical Society of America)*

The ability of a laser cavity to maintain laser action is influenced by the Fresnel number for the optical cavity:

$$F = \frac{\omega_1 \omega_2}{d}$$

where F is the Fresnel number, ω_1 and ω_2 are the radius of the beam at the cavity mirrors, and d is the separation of mirrors. For $F < 1$ the cavity is unstable, $F > 2$ the cavity is stable.

References

1. Kaspar, S., 'Radiometry', *American Institute of Physics Handbook*, Ed. D. E. Gray, pp. 198–221, McGraw-Hill, New York, 1972.
2. Kogelnik, H. and Li, T., 'Laser Beams and Resonators', *Appl. Opt.*, **5** (10), 1550–1567, 1966.

2

LASER CHARACTERISTICS

The characteristics of lasers have been extensively studied as they represent both singly and collectively a completely new type of light source with properties not previously achievable by any other source. Several general references dealing exclusively with lasers are given in the selected reading list at the end of the book. Here we are concerned with the properties that affect the application of lasers of which the most important characteristics are:

    (a) Output wavelength
    (b) Divergence
    (c) Mode structure
    (d) Coherence
    (e) Polarization
    (f) Energy and power output.

Many of these are possessed to varying degrees by most lasers. Table 2.1 lists some of these characteristics together with the applications for which they are required and the type of laser normally used.

2.1 Output wavelength

The wavelength of the output of a laser is not truly monochromatic but normally has a very much narrower bandwidth at a considerably higher intensity than that obtainable from thermal sources. This is illustrated schematically in Fig. 2.1 in which the relative intensities of a black body, electric discharge, fluorescent source and a laser are shown. The output wavelength depends on the energy level of the transitions involved and the resonant wavelengths of the optical cavity. Electron transitions in neutral-atom, solid-state, and semiconductor lasers result in outputs in the visible region and near infrared, the output of ion lasers is in the visible and near ultraviolet. The output wavelengths from lower energy molecular transitions is generally in the middle and far infrared region of the spectrum extending over broad bands. The principal range of operating wavelengths of the different types of lasers is shown in

Table 2.1 *Principal laser characteristics required for different applications*

Application	Monochromatic	Low Divergence	Single or low order Mode	Coherence	High output power	Efficiency	Laser Normally Used
Precision measurement of length	✓		✓	✓			He–Ne
Surveying and alignment	✓	✓					He–Ne
Range-finding		✓			✓		Nd:YAG, GaAs
Velocity measurement	✓						He–Ne
Drilling	✓	✓			✓	✓	Ruby, Nd:YAG
Cutting	✓	✓			✓	✓	CO_2
Welding	✓	✓			✓	✓	CO_2, ruby, Nd:YAG
Ophthalmology	✓	✓					Ruby, argon ion
Pollution detection	✓						Dye, GaAs
Holography	✓		✓	✓			Ruby, Nd:YAG, Argon ion, He–Ne
Communications	✓	✓		✓			He–Ne, GaAs

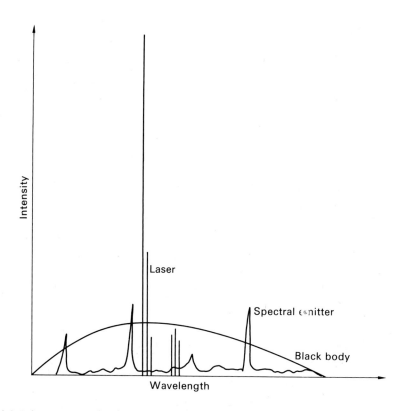

Fig. 2.1 *Relative intensity distribution of a black body, electric discharge, fluorescent source, and a laser*

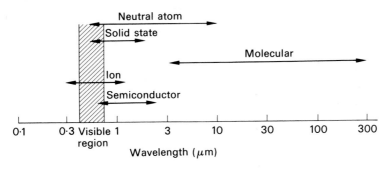

Fig. 2.2 *Laser types and their range of wavelengths*

Fig. 2.2. The very large number of output wavelengths from different lasers have been tabulated for the various types of lasers.[1]

The output wavelength often extends over one or more narrow bands of wavelengths corresponding to different laser transitions or in the case of a dye laser a broad continuous band (continuum). A characteristic wavelength is normally used to describe the mean wavelength of the output of a laser corresponding to a particular transition. The cavity is normally long compared with $\lambda_0/2$ the laser can resonate at a number of wavelengths within a band at intervals of $\lambda_0/2$ corresponding to the bandwidth of the laser transitions. Fluctuations in the length of the cavity (due to expansion for example) will result in changes in λ_0. Selection of a very narrow band of wavelengths is often possible and a very high resolution of $d\lambda/\lambda_0 < 10^{-4}$ can be achieved in some cases.

The comparatively high output intensity concentrated over a narrow band of wavelength readily obtainable from most lasers is greatly in excess of that possible from other light sources. This is important in many laser applications in which a narrow band of wavelengths is used, such as in metrology, or where discrimination from background illumination is required. An important indirect advantage of the narrow band of output wavelengths obtained is the elimination of chromatic aberration in laser optical systems.

The output frequency can be doubled or quadrupled corresponding to $\lambda_0/2$ or $\lambda_0/4$ by frequency conversion in a suitable non-linear optical material. Useful outputs are obtainable in the visible region, by frequency doubling the output of lasers in the near infrared. Outputs in the ultraviolet can be obtained by frequency doubling the output of lasers in the visible region and quadrupling the output frequency of lasers with outputs in the near infrared. (See Section 3.2.3.)

2.2 Divergence

Conventional light sources radiate more or less uniformly in all directions and the intensity falls off as the inverse square of the distance. Any attempt to produce a parallel beam, for example with a refracting or reflecting collimator, is only partly successful. The finite size of practical light sources results in light other than at the focus of the collimator being focused off axis by the collimator. A second source of divergence is due to diffraction which occurs at the boundaries of apertures which exist in any practical focusing system. The use of apertures to confine a beam to rays closely parallel to the optical axis of a collimator is limited by divergence due to diffraction. The relative magnitudes of the effects of the finite size of the light source and divergence due to apertures will vary depending on the geometry of the system.

Usually in the laser the region of high intensity is remote from the geometrical boundaries of the walls of the resonant cavity and edges of the aperture (output window). Since amplification is necessary requiring many passes along the cavity, only light very closely parallel to the optic axis of the laser emerges. The angle of spread is now determined by the special properties of the laser beam rather than by the boundaries of the system (Fig. 2.3). In the limiting case this is governed by the inherent diffraction of the beam itself. The divergence of multi-mode lasers is higher than single mode lasers.

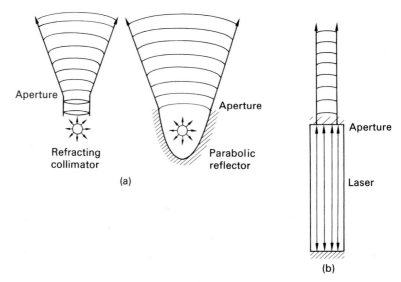

Fig. 2.3 *Divergence due to diffraction of:* (a) *conventional light source with refracting or reflecting collimator ;*
(b) *laser*

The small divergence of laser light measured in terms of the half angle of spread (of the order of a few milliradians) is an important characteristic of laser emission. The low divergence enables the apertures of optical components to be kept within reasonable limits compared with those that would be required for conventional light sources and the beam intensity is such that it can be readily detected over long distances which is important for such applications as surveying, range finding, pollution detection, and communications.

Beam divergence is normally measured in terms of the half angle subtended by the diverging beam. The beam divergence can be reduced by expanding and collimating the beam by a factor inversely proportional to the diameter of the expanded beam.

The divergence is also dependent on the laser mirrors; spherical mirrors and output windows result in a higher divergence of the laser beam than for plane mirrors.

The radius of the laser beam is normally measured as half the distance between points at which the amplitude is $1/e$ (0·368) that of the centre, and the intensity (power density) is $1/e^2$ (0·135). This is illustrated for a Gaussian distribution in Fig. 2.4 where

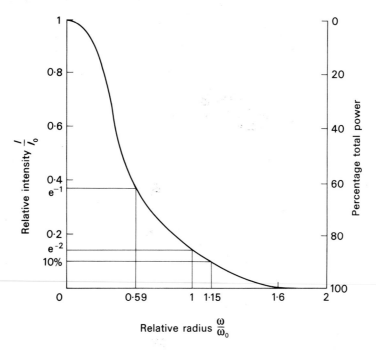

Fig. 2.4 *Variation of relative intensity and percentage total power with radius for a Gaussian beam*

the amplitude is given by

$$A = A_0 e^{-\omega^2/\omega_0^2}$$

and the intensity

$$I = I_0 e^{-2\omega^2/\omega_0^2}$$

where A_0 and I_0 are the peak amplitudes and intensity at the centre of the beam and ω_0 is the radius at the window. Alternative measures of the beam radius are occasionally used.

The divergence of a diffraction-limited beam from a laser with a plain output window can be calculated by considering it in terms of a lens with object distance zero and focus at infinity[2] which gives

$$\omega_2 = \omega_0 \left[1 + \left(\frac{d\lambda}{\pi\omega_0^2} \right)^2 \right]^{\frac{1}{2}}$$

where ω_2 is the radius of the beam at a distance d from the laser window. At large values of d

$$\omega_2 \approx \omega_0 \frac{d\lambda}{(\pi\omega_0^2)}$$

and the divergence

$$\alpha = \frac{2}{\pi} \frac{\lambda}{\omega_0}$$

15

2.3 Mode structure

Inside the laser cavity the electromagnetic field generated by the stimulated emission process, is constrained to take up certain allowed configurations (modes) consistent with the boundary conditions.

Ideally light would be emitted corresponding to the amplification of only one transition so that it was temporally coherent. In practice, the light from several transitions often occurs including longitudinal modes resulting from more than one axial mode and transverse modes caused by reflections from the side walls of the cavity. This means that the emitted light comes out in certain preferred distributions. The beam may then consist of a spot, or of other more complicated shapes some of which are illustrated in Fig. 2.5.

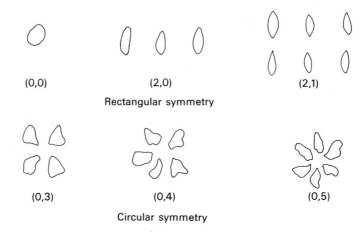

(0,0)   (2,0)   (2,1)

Rectangular symmetry

(0,3)   (0,4)   (0,5)

Circular symmetry

Fig. 2.5 *Examples of rectangular and circularly symmetrical modes*

The boundary conditions (shape of mirror, diameter of tube, etc.) allow only certain 'modes' of vibration, each of which has its own characteristic intensity distribution, many of which have been analysed.[3] The laser output consists of a superimposition of allowed modes. In low-power gas lasers there is often either only one mode, or a very few so that one can see at a glance which modes are present. In high-power systems many modes may be superimposed and it may be difficult to resolve the output in terms of individual modes.

Each observed mode has a different frequency, so that by examining the distribution of the intensity in the output beam one can in principle see not only what modes are in oscillation but also how many different frequencies there are in the output.

The laser mode structure is important for many applications. A stable mode structure is important for communications, interferometric measurement of distance, and holography. For some fabrication processes it is desirable that the output should be of a single spatial mode so that the diffraction-limited focused beam diameter can be achieved corresponding to the highest power densities in the laser beam.

Factors that affect the mode structure include the geometry of the laser cavity and optics, the gain of the cavity, inhomogeneities in the laser medium, and the pumping power. Reflection from cavity walls tends to enhance high order longitudinal and circumferential (whispering†) modes, whereas diffraction losses in long cavities with a low Fresnel number (see also section 1.4) attenuate high-order modes. Spatial coherence is dependent on the stability of the mode structure transverse to the laser axes while the stability of the longitudinal mode determines the temporal coherence. Analyses of laser cavities and mode structures have been made for a variety of conditions.

The classification of the mode structure is based on the distribution of the output in a similar way to that used to describe modes in a waveguide at microwave frequencies corresponding to the axis of the transverse electrostatic (TE) and transverse electromagnetic (TEM) fields, and is best illustrated by reference to Fig. 2.5. The intensity distribution shown is in the plane perpendicular to the plane in which the mode distribution lies.

Modes with rectangular symmetry can often be obtained from cavities that have cylindrical symmetry. This is particularly true of gas lasers. Although the outer geometry of the cavity may be circular the individual nodes within the cavity, once established, are small compared with the dimensions of the mirrors. As a result the intensity at the edge of the mirror is very small so that the effect of the geometry of the walls of the cavity is small and the mode structure may be more dependent on other factors. Both rectangular and circular modes can normally be obtained from the same cavity by varying its parameters.

The designation of the mode number where rectangular symmetry exists is normally based on the convention that the first subscript refers to the mode number on the x axis, the second subscript to the y axis. The mode number is always one higher than the number of illuminated zones. The zero-order mode which ideally has a Gaussian distribution is designated TEM_{00}. Two regions of maximum intensity correspond to the second-order mode TEM_{10} and three along one axis to TEM_{20}. Similarly if an output zone exists on the y axis as in Fig. 2.5 then this becomes TEM_{21}. Where circular symmetry exists the first subscript represents the radial mode, the second the azimuthal mode.

Mode selection is possible by varying the mirror curvature and by including apertures with or without additional lenses, resonant reflectors or saturable absorbers within the optical cavity. Single-mode operation is generally more easily obtained when the gain is not sufficient for amplification of less efficient high-order modes. Preferential amplification of the single-order mode can be achieved by using an oscillator amplifier configuration in which the single mode output from a low-power laser (oscillator) is amplified in a second cavity which is pumped in the same way but has no mirrors so that only amplification of the first-order mode occurs.

2.4 Coherence

The term coherence is used to describe different parts of an assembly of electromagnetic waves which are in phase with one another. The terms spatial and temporal coherence are often used to refer to the output of lasers. Spatial coherence is a term which describes the phase relation in a plane perpendicular to the direction of propagation; temporal

---

† Whispering modes are analogous to the multiple reflections of sound waves in circular galleries such as in St Paul's Cathedral, sometimes known as whispering galleries.

coherence describes the phase relation in the direction of the beam. For some applications such as holography, both temporal and spatial coherence are required, others such as laser interferometry require temporal coherence only, whereas some fabrication processes require spatial coherence. Applications such as alignment require neither.

If a beam is coherent then when two parts of it are combined an interference pattern is produced. Both the temporal and spatial coherence can be examined in this way.

A requirement for perfect temporal coherence is that the output should be monochromatic. Since this is never achieved exactly in practice, the degree of temporal coherence is limited. The degree of temporal coherence is often described by the coherence length which is the distance (from the output window of the laser) over which the output intensity retains a measurable correlation of phase. Since all lasers have a relatively narrow bandwidth (unlike most other light sources) a limited degree of temporal coherence usually exists over a distance varying from a few millimetres to several metres while the coherence length of ordinary thermal light sources is too short to be measured. The degree to which the frequency of the longitudinal mode is stable is the limiting factor governing the coherence length. The stability of the longitudinal mode is limited by fluctuations in mirror geometry, thermal variation in the laser medium, and changes of the mirror separation. Methods using feedback to compensate for fluctuations in cavity length can be used. The need for a large coherence length has limited the application of holography to relatively small objects up to now.

Spatial coherence on the other hand can be achieved from thermal sources by suitable artifices. The output of lasers may be fully spatially coherent or almost non-coherent, depending on the design of the cavity. A single mode or uni-phase laser has only one longitudinal and transverse mode and is fully spatially coherent.

2.5 Polarization

The behaviour of a light ray can be described in terms of an electric vibration and a magnetic vibration at right angles to each other and perpendicular to the direction of propagation of the ray (Fig. 2.6). The ray is said to be plane polarized since the electric vibration is in only one plane. By superimposing other rays with polarization planes

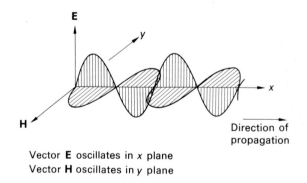

Vector **E** oscillates in x plane
Vector **H** oscillates in y plane

Fig. 2.6 Electric and magnetic field intensities associated with a ray of light

18

in different directions a randomly polarized beam may result. Alternatively if the direction of polarization is ordered more complex forms of polarization such as elliptical and circular polarization can be obtained. A more detailed treatment of polarization is given in the books on geometrical and physical optics listed in the selected reading list at the end of the book.

The output of a laser may be polarized or unpolarized. Polarized light is useful in some laser applications, in particular where the output is modulated or used together with bi-refringent optical materials. A polarized beam can be achieved from an unpolarized laser beam by using suitable polarizing materials; however a reduction in intensity of the light output occurs.

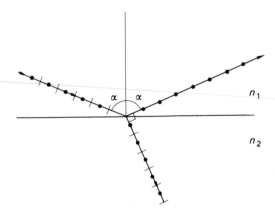

Fig. 2.7 *Complete polarization by reflection at the Brewster angle*

Polarization by refraction at the interface between two materials of different refractive indices is also possible. Polarization by refraction is greatest when the angle of incidence of the beam is equal to the Brewster angle at which the angle between the reflected and refracted ray is $90°$, as shown in Fig. 2.7. This occurs when the tangent of the angle of incidence is equal to the refractive index of the material. (For an air–glass interface this corresponds to an angle of $57°$.) At this angle the reflected ray is completely polarized in the plane of incidence which is indicated by dots on the reflected ray and the refracted ray has a proportionately higher degree of polarization in the plane perpendicular to the plane of incidence indicated by dashes perpendicular to the plane of the refracted ray.

The end faces of solid-state lasers or windows of gas lasers may be cut at the Brewster angle to minimize internal reflections where external optics are used or where a polarized output is required. The reflected ray polarized in the plane perpendicular to the plane of incidence is not reflected along the axis of the laser and has little effect on the amplification in the cavity. The refracted beam is reflected back along its path by the external mirror and the degree of polarization in the plane of incidence is increased as it is transmitted through the end face and on subsequent transmissions. As a result a highly polarized output beam is achieved. The end faces may be parallel or anti-parallel, the anti-parallel configuration allowing the mirrors to be mounted on a common axis.

2.6 Energy and power output

The output of a laser may be continuous, normally referred to as CW (continuous wave), or pulsed. What is apparently a single pulse on close inspection may be found to comprise a series of pulses of much shorter duration. The pulsed output may vary from a single pulse to a series of repetitive pulses to give a quasi-continuous output (as opposed to a true CW output).

The power is expressed in watts and since the duration of the pulse may be very short the power output can be very large, of the order of several megawatts, although the total energy in the pulse in joules may be very small. For example, an output pulse of ten nanoseconds (10^{-8} s) duration and total energy one millijoule (10^{-3} J) corresponds to a mean power of one megawatt (10^5W).

The magnitude of the power output (CW and pulsed) is governed by various factors including the laser transition and the method and intensity of excitation, the diameter and length of the laser and the rate at which heat can be dissipated in the laser host and pumping source. The power output also depends on the overall gain of the cavity which in turn depends on the intensity of pumping, absorption losses, reflectivity of the output window, and other cavity parameters.

The power output of solid-state lasers is a function of the volume of the laser material and the illuminated surface area which is usually proportional to length, the diameter being limited due to absorption of the pumping radiation by the host. The power output of gas lasers is a function of the excited volume. The maximum

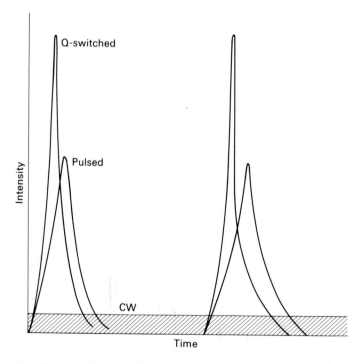

Fig. 2.8 *Variation of intensity with time of CW, pulsed, and Q-switched laser output for the same total energy dissipation*

diameter is usually limited by the discharge but may also be a function of the wavelength, too large a diameter resulting in unwanted whispering modes.

The duration of the output of pulsed lasers is often important. The pulse length can be varied over a wide range from nanoseconds for Q-switched and mode-locked outputs up to several milliseconds depending on the laser transition by using pulse-shaping networks in the supply circuit. The relative intensities of repetitively pulsed and Q-switched outputs together with a CW output are illustrated in Fig. 2.8. The output power intensity decreases as the pulse length increases and the total pulse energy remains approximately constant.

Optically pumped lasers are normally operated in the pulsed mode and are difficult to pump at high powers continuously. A high continuous output is required from the discharge tubes used to pump the laser and to overcome the threshold level and counteract the high cavity losses. The high threshold and low efficiency result in high thermal dissipation in the laser rod. Gas and liquid lasers can generally be operated with either pulsed or continuous outputs or repetitively pulsed to give a quasi-continuous output. The pumping efficiency of gas lasers is often higher than that for solid-state lasers. Continuous-flow lasers in which the laser medium is efficiently cooled enable very high powers to be achieved.

The power output may be increased by Q-switching which is achieved by exciting the laser medium so that a population inversion occurs but delaying the application of feedback from the axial mirrors.[4] This can be achieved by deflecting the beam at the totally reflecting mirror mechanically or by accousto-optic or electro-optic devices or by using an opaque dye solution that bleaches transparent when the fluorescent light output reaches a given level. Output pulses of large amplitudes with rapid rise times (i.e., the maximum intensity is rapidly reached) are obtained since most of the excited states decay in a very short time. Repetitive Q switching of pulsed and repetitively pulsed CW lasers is also possible.

The output of a laser often consists of many modes which bear no fixed relation to each other. If the output modes are forced to maintain equal frequency spacings and fixed phase relations to each other the output will vary with time in a well-defined manner and is said to be phase-locked or mode-locked.

If several axial modes are locked together in phase the peak intensity will be correspondingly higher than that obtained from the sum of individual modes randomly related to each other. Mode locking can be used to obtain very high output powers of selected modes of laser emission which retain their frequency and phase relation. This sometimes occurs naturally (self mode locking) but can also be achieved by selective saturation causing bleaching for example of a dye cell.[5] Other techniques for mode locking are also possible. Preferential modes can be selected by eliminating unwanted reflections using Brewster windows and apertures within the optical cavity. Since the feedback corresponds only to the preferred mode the build-up of stimulated emission is very rapid and higher pulse amplitudes with more rapid rise times are obtained than by Q switching.

The stability of the output in terms of the repeatability of the amplitude and duration of the output from pulsed lasers is often important. This is partly governed by the power supply and method of initiating the pulse so that the energy supplied to the flash tubes or laser electrodes is the same at each pulse. Increase in temperature of the laser material changes the relative populations of the energy levels. Expansion of the cavity causes variations in mode structure and wavelength and misalignment of optics which affect the stability. The progressive deterioration of flash and continuous discharge tubes, sputtering of electrode material, and gas leaks in gas laser cavities also affect the repeatability of the laser output.

2.7 Energy transfer and efficiency

The efficiency of lasers can be defined in terms of

$$\eta = \frac{\text{energy output in the laser beam}}{\text{total energy input}}$$

and is known as the overall efficiency. This is dependent on external factors, such as losses in power supplies, pumps, refrigerating systems, and other auxilliary devices as well as the laser itself. In the final assessment of a complete system, the overall efficiency is often important. To compare the relative efficiency of lasers the conversion efficiency defined as

$$\eta' = \frac{\text{energy output in the laser beam}}{\text{excitation energy input}}$$

is useful.

The excitation energy input is the energy input to the electrodes of a CW laser (in the case of gas or semiconductor lasers), or the energy input to the pumping light source in the case of solid-state lasers.

As well as the overall efficiency the slope efficiency is also important. The slope efficiency is the incremental efficiency as the power is increased above the threshold value. The slope efficiency at high powers may be several times that close to the threshold level, but decreases as saturation of the laser medium occurs.

The energy losses may be sub-divided into external losses, which may result in costly systems and high running costs but otherwise do not normally limit the operation of the laser, and internal losses in the laser cavity itself which may limit the maximum operating conditions to the rate at which the thermal energy can be dissipated.

Some typical values of power losses are tabulated for pulsed and CW gas and solid state lasers in table 2.2. Pulsed lasers using energy stored in capacitors result in more than half the stored energy being dissipated in the output leads and the capacitor itself. This can be minimized by decreasing the series impedance; however, if optical excitation is used it may be necessary to increase the impedance to prevent oscillation which causes excessive electrode erosion.

The net conversion efficiency of a discharge lamp may be as high as 60 per cent to 80 per cent; however, some of this is dissipated in the walls of the tube at wavelengths in the ultraviolet and infrared. Of the light transmitted by the envelope only part will contribute to the absorption bands of the laser material, typically of the order of 25 per cent.

Part of the energy absorbed in the laser rod (60 per cent in the case of a ruby) may be dissipated in unwanted transitions. Of the energy absorbed by the laser levels 25 per cent may be dissipated within the laser rod due to absorption by impurities, scattering due to inhomogeneties, inclusions, and diffraction losses. The maximum total overall

Table 2.2 *Loss processes for solid-state and gas lasers*

	Percentage Loss			
Loss Process	Solid-State Lasers		Gas Laser	
	Pulsed	CW	Pulsed	CW
Power Source (% total input power)				
Charging circuit	> 50	—	> 50	—
Discharge circuit	> 50	> 50	> 50	> 50
Pumping process (% input power at electrodes)				
Losses in discharge tube walls	10–50	10–50	—	—
Losses at discharge tube electrodes	∼ 10	∼ 10	—	—
Losses at laser electrodes	—	—	∼ 10	∼ 10
Losses at discharge tube reflectors	∼ 10	∼ 10	—	—
Absorption by non-laser transitions	90–99·9	90–99·9	80–99	80–99
Cavity (% total laser power)				
Losses at total reflecting mirror	∼ 1	∼ 1	∼ 1	∼ 1
Losses at output window	∼ 1	∼ 1	∼ 1	∼ 1

efficiency of conversion of the energy stored in the pulsed power supply is therefore around 0·01–1 per cent.

The losses corresponding to the conversion of input power to light output will not apply in the case of pulsed or continuous gas lasers. If the efficiency of the power supply is high as in the case of a continuous gas laser using inductive reactance for stabilization of the discharge then the efficiency depends primarily on the percentage of the input energy that is absorbed by required transitions. Typically the efficiency of gas lasers is about 0·1 per cent but for a CO_2 laser this can be up to 18 per cent.

References

1. Pressley, R. J. (Ed.), *Handbook of Lasers*, The Chemical Rubber Co, Ohio, 1971.
2. Dickson, L. D., 'Characteristics of a Propagating Laser Beam', *Appl. Opt.*, **9** (8), 1854–1861, 1970.
3. Kogelnik, H. and Li, T., 'Laser Beams and Resonators', *Appl. Opt.*, **5** (10), 1550–1567, 1966.
4. Hellworth, R. W., 'Q Modulation of Lasers', *Lasers* Vol. I Chapter 4, Ed. A. K. Lavine, Edward Arnold, London; Marcel Dekker, New York, 1966.

3

MATERIALS AND COMPONENTS USED IN LASER SYSTEMS

A wide variety of materials have useful optical properties and the properties of a large number of these are summarized in the *American Institute of Physics Handbook*.[1]

Many of these materials have only a very limited number of applications and it is outside the scope of this book to consider in detail the properties of every optical material. This chapter considers only those materials commonly encountered in lasers and associated optical systems, the reasons for their choice, and a summary of their properties.

3.1 Optical properties of materials

A large number of materials have useful transmitting properties at optical wavelengths. These include transmitting materials for use as windows, lenses, and prisms, bi-refringent materials for polarization and beam splitters, electro-optic, accousto-optic, and magneto-optic materials for modulation, and materials for harmonic generation and parametric modulation.

Common properties of interest are the transmission band, the absorption co-efficient, and the refractive index. The solubility in water is often important where the material is used in ambient conditions where ambient moisture or condensed water vapour may damage the highly polished surface. Many of the materials that have useful transmission properties are water soluble to varying degrees and in some cases require protection. Properties which also influence their selection include the modulus of elasticity, thermal conductivity, coefficient of expansion, softening and melting points, and density. The form in which the material is available, ease of optical working, hardness, and resistance to thermal and mechanical shock may also be important.

The transmission band is normally expressed as the limit between the cut-off points at long and short wavelengths at which the external transmittance decreases to 10 per cent. The external transmittance is defined as the transmittance of the sample of a given thickness and includes losses due to reflection at the first and second surfaces. Absorption over the transmission band is normally very small, although narrow absorption bands sometimes due to the presence of impurities may exist. For most transmitting materials, losses due to absorption can be considered as negligible over the transmission band ($\ll$ 1 per cent) compared with losses due to reflection. At high-pulsed and CW power levels absorption may cause damage to optical components.

The variation of transmission with wavelength is normally expressed in terms of the external transmittance and includes reflection losses. As a result, although large differences in external transmittance may exist for different materials corresponding to different refractive indices, the absorption may be negligible in both cases. Since in most cases the external transmittance can be increased to nearly 100 per cent by the application of anti-reflection coatings, the external transmittance characteristic is of most use in defining the transmission band and showing the position of absorption bands, if they exist.

The attenuation is given by

$$I = I_0 e^{-kx} \tag{3.1}$$

where k is the absorption coefficient. The absorption coefficient can be obtained from the external transmittance if the thickness and the reflection loss are known.

As well as the bulk absorption it is also necessary to consider surface absorption in the case of hygroscopic materials used in ambient conditions.

The reflection loss occurs at the interface between two materials of different refractive indices. The first surface reflection loss at normal incidence is given by

$$\left(\frac{n-1}{n+1}\right)^2 \tag{3.2}$$

where n is the ratio of the refractive index of the second material to the first. Since we are usually concerned with systems in air, n is normally the refractive index of the material relative to air. Reflection loss at the second interface will often be a second-order effect and therefore can be ignored.

The reflection loss for different incidence angles and refractive indices for un-polarized light is shown in Fig. 3.1.[2] The reflection loss for light polarized in the plane perpendicular to the plane of incidence and parallel to it, is also shown for $n = 1.5$ (glass). No reflection loss occurs for light polarized perpendicular to the plane of incidence at the Brewster angle. The reflection losses at other angles of incidence and degrees of polarization can be determined from the Fresnel equation for reflection. For glass ($n = 1.5$) the reflection loss is less than 5 per cent and can sometimes be ignored; however, for a material such as germanium ($n = 4$) the reflection loss at the first surface is 25 per cent.

The reflection that occurs at the interface between materials of different refractive indices is often a disadvantage in optical systems. It can be reduced by separating the two materials by one or more layers of intermediate refractive index and anti-reflection coatings comprising several layers may be used in this way (see section 3.1.2). Such coatings are sometimes referred to as dielectric coatings as they are normally electric insulators.

Where complete absorption takes place when reflection losses at the first surface are included

$$I = (1-\beta)\, I_0 e^{-kx} \tag{3.3}$$

25

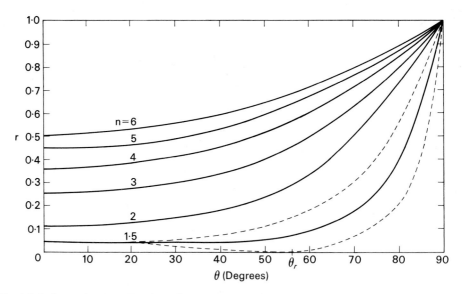

Fig. 3.1 *Reflection loss for different incidence angles and different refractive indices (from Holter, M. R., Nudelman, S., Suits, G. H., Wolfe, W. L. and Zissis, G. J.,* Fundamentals of Infra-red Technology, *Macmillan, New York, 1962)*

where β is the coefficient of reflectivity. The external transmittance where partial absorption occurs and the reflection at the second interface is small (so that the net light transmitted after further reflection is negligible) is given by

$$T = \frac{I_t}{I_0} = (1 - \beta')^2 \mathrm{e}^{-kd}$$

$$(3.4)$$

where β' is the reflection coefficient at the second interface. The refractive index varies with wavelength (dispersion) and is shown for selected optical materials in Fig. 3.2.[3] The refractive indices for a large number of optical materials have been tabulated as functions of the wavelength together with other parameters affecting the refractive index.[1]

3.1.1 Window and lens materials The transmission band over which the external transmittance of a sample 2 mm thick is greater than 10 per cent and typical values of refractive indices of optically transmitting materials used for windows and lenses are tabulated in table 3.1. Most of these materials are commercially available in forms suitable for optical windows, lenses and other components. The refractive index of materials depends on the wavelength of the light. This phenomenon is called dispersion. The refractive indices for a large number of optical materials have been tabulated as a function of wavelength and other parameters.[1] The variation of refractive indices with wavelength of some selected optical materials is shown in Fig. 3.2.[3]

This section primarily considers those materials that have been used with lasers. The properties of many of the other materials have been summarized in reference 1.

The most widely used optical materials for windows and lenses in the range extending from 0·15 µm to 2 µm over which helium–neon, argon, helium–cadmium,

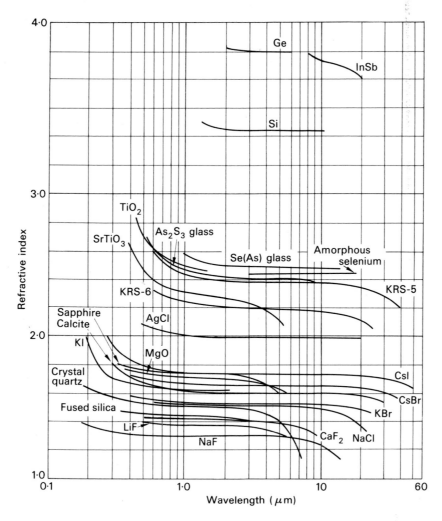

Fig. 3.2 *Refractive indices of preferred optical materials (from Wolfe, W. L. and Ballard, S. S., 'Optical Materials, Films and Filters for Infra-red Instrumentation', Proc. IRE, **47** (9), 1590–1545, 1959)*

ruby, and neodymium lasers operate are various forms of silica glass.

Representative commercial glasses are soda lime, lead alkali and borosilicate glasses based on silicon dioxide. Soda lime glass comprises about 72 per cent SiO_2 with about 12 per cent Na_2O and 10 per cent CaO with small quantities of about 1 per cent of MgO and Al_2O_3. Lead alkali silicates contain up to 58 per cent PbO and aluminosilicate up to 20 per cent Al_2O_3. Various other oxides may be present depending on the application. Borosilicate glasses contain around 67–80 per cent SiO_2 with between 12 and 30 per cent of B_2O_2 with small quantities of other oxides.

The optical transmission of glass is dependent on its constituents and purity which vary over wide ranges.[4] The normal limits of transmission of optical glasses are shown in Fig. 3.3. Where transmission closest to the upper or lower limits is required, the transmission will depend on the precise formulation of the glass constituents. The

Table 3.1 *Properties of window and lens materials*

Material	Refractive Index	Transmission Band (μm) 0·1 0·5 1 5 10 50	Comments
Arsenic modified selenium glass	2·48		Similar properties to amorphous selenium but softens at 70°C
Arsenic trisulphide glass, As_2S_3	2·6		Soft. Insoluble in water
Barium fluoride, BaF_2	1·42		Good transmission in UV. Brittle. Slightly soluble in water
Barium fluoride/calcium fluoride (T-12) BaF_2/CaF_2	1·41		Good transmission in IR uncoated. Good resistance to thermal shock. Slightly soluble in water
Barium titanate, $BaTiO_3$	2·4		Good transmission in IR. Hard. Insoluble in water
Borosilicate glass	1·49–1·55		Limited transmission in UV and IR. Good resistance to thermal shock. Not soluble in water
Cadmium sulphide, Cds	2·15		Relatively soft. Not soluble in water
Cadmium telluride (Irtran 6), CdTe	2·56		Good transmission in IR. Hard. Insoluble in water
Cesium bromide, CsBr	1·66		Good transmission in IR. Highly soluble in water
Cesium iodide, CsI	1·79		Good transmission in IR. Relatively soft. Highly soluble in water
Calcium fluoride (Irtran 3), CaF_2	1·43		Good transmission in UV uncoated. Hard. Low solubility in water
Calcium aluminate glass	1·7–1·8		Useful transmission in IR. Hard. Insoluble in water
Gallium arsenide, GaAs	3·14		Useful transmission properties in IR. Operation at higher power densities than Ge. Insoluble in water
Germanium, Ge	4·04		Useful transmission properties in IR. Brittle. Insoluble in water
Lithium fluoride, LiF	1·35		Useful UV properties uncoated. Brittle. Insoluble in water
Magnesium fluoride (Irtran 1), MgF_2	1·34		Good transmission in IR uncoated. Relatively hard. Insoluble in water
Magnesium oxide (Irtran 5), MgO	1·72		Good transmission in IR. Hard. Insoluble in water
Polymethyl methacrylate	1·49		Relatively good transmission properties in near UV and IR. Soft. Insoluble in water

0·1 0·5 1 5 10 50

Table 3.1 *Properties of window and lens materials (continued)*

Material	Refractive Index	Transmission Band (μm) 0·1 0·5 1 5 10 50	Comments
Potassium bromide, KBr	1·54		Good transmission properties in UV and IR. Very soluble in water
Potassium chloride, KCl	1·49		Good transmission properties in UV and IR. Soluble in water
Potassium iodide, KI	1·67		Good transmission properties in UV and IR. Soft. Highly soluble in water
Quartz (fused), SiO$_2$	1·40–1·57		Good transmission properties in near UV and IR. High thermal resistance to shock. Insoluble in water
Sapphire, Al$_2$O$_3$	1·77		Very high resistance to damage at high powers. Insoluble in water
Selenium (amorphous), Se	2·46		Good IR transmission. Softens at 35°C. Insoluble in water
Silicon, Si	3·41		High resistance to thermal shock. Insoluble in water
Silver chloride, AgCl	2·07		Very soft. Easily deformed. Insoluble in water
Sodium chloride, NaCl	1·54		Good transmission properties in UV and IR. Highly soluble in water
Sodium fluoride, NaF	1·33		Very low refractive index. Low solubility in water
Spinel, MgO.3·5Al$_2$O$_3$	1·69		Easier to work optically than sapphire but reduced transmission. Hard. Insoluble in water
Strontium titanate, SrTiO$_3$	2·15		Good transmission in IR. Hard. Insoluble in water
Thallium bromide, TlBr	2·2		Difficult to work optically. Slightly soluble in water. Poisonous.
Thallium bromide iodide (KRS-5) TlBr/TlI	2·37		Good IR transmission properties. soluble in water. Poisonous
Thallium chloride, TlCl	2·25		Difficult to work optically
Thallium chloride bromide (KRS-6) TlCl/TlBr	2·34		Similar properties to KRS-5. Better transmission in UV. Poisonous
Titanium dioxide (rutile), TiO$_2$	2·6–2·9		Limited transmission in IR
Zinc selenide (Irtran 4), ZnSe	2·5		Good transmission in UV and IR. Hard. Insoluble in water
Zinc sulphide (Irtran 2), ZnS	2·3		Good transmission in IR. Relatively hard. Insoluble in water.

0·1   0·5   1   5   10   50

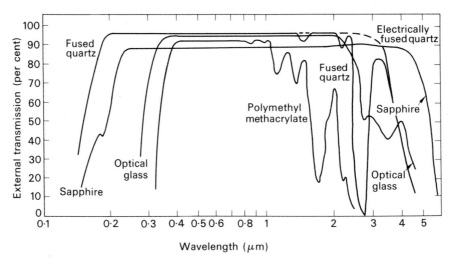

Fig. 3.3 *The external transmission of optical glass, fused silica, sapphire and polymethyl methacrylate (2 mm thick)*

absorption that occurs in the infrared at about 2·7 μm is partly due to the hydroxyl ion (OH) which is introduced during manufacture by flame fusion processes. This can be reduced by electric melting.

The transmission of high purity fused silica is also shown in Fig. 3.3. The transmission of fused silica is better than that of glass at long and short wavelengths, but is also dependent on the purity, particularly at short wavelengths. At long wavelengths absorption occurs due to the hydroxyl ion which also can be reduced by electric melting. The transmission of electrically fused high purity silica is also shown in Fig. 3.3.

Fused silica has a high melting point, low coefficient of expansion and high transmission in the ultraviolet region. The absorption coefficient is dependent on the purity and is very much less than that for natural quartz crystal. Absorption coefficients $\ll 0\cdot01/\text{mm}$ are obtainable for fused silica of high purity.

The choice of glass is dependent on the transmission at low powers and at high powers is also dependent on the damage threshold. At very high powers such as occur in Q switched and mode locked lasers the damage threshold becomes the most important criterion. This is normally limited in commercial glasses by particulate impurities which cause local absorption. Typical damage thresholds for high purity commercial glasses are 10^7W/mm^2 to 10^8W/mm^2.

Sapphire (Al_2O_3) has good transmission over the visible and near infrared region (Fig. 3.3) and can be used at high peak powers where the very high polish obtainable results in a high threshold of thermal damage at the surface. Sapphire is also used for first surface reflection where the refractive index ($n \doteq 1\cdot7$) which is higher than quartz or glass enables a higher reflectivity to be obtained.

The refractive index of silica-based glasses varies with wavelength and composition. Reflection at an air–glass interface is less than 5 per cent, and it is not always necessary to coat glass optics. Where a single layer coating is required, a quarter-wave coating of magnesium fluoride ($n = 1\cdot38$) is often used, although other coating materials may also be used (see section 3.1.2). The use of coatings at high continuous powers, and when used for Q switched or pulsed applications, is restricted since power dissipation in the coating may damage it.

Although not commonly used for optical components in laser systems various plastics[4] and in particular acrylic resins have relatively good optical transmission properties in the visible and near infrared. The external transmittance of polymethyl methacrylate is also shown in Fig. 3.3. While capable of transmitting only relatively low power densities over its transmission range it can be used as a screen to block indirect radiation at wavelengths outside its transmission range.

Outside the visible region and the near infrared and ultraviolet no universally suitable materials comparable with glass in the visible region exist. The transmission of many of the available materials is limited to relatively narrow bands and the combination of properties is such that a critical evaluation has to be made for each application. The alkali halides, bromides, fluorides, and iodides have good transmission properties over broad bands[5] but are often soluble in water and deteriorate when unprotected under normal ambient conditions while the refractive index of the semiconductor materials is high, requiring the use of anti-reflection coatings.

Glass-like crystalline materials but which are not based on silica, such as arsenic trisulphide and arsenic modified selenium glasses and calcium aluminate glass, have been used to extend the useful range of transmission further into the near infrared region.[6] The properties of some of these glasses are shown in Table 3.1.

Silicon has good transmission properties over the range 1·5 μm–5 μm which covers the output of the helium–neon laser at 3·39 μm and several molecular lasers, and is capable of withstanding high power densities. The variation of the external transmission with wavelength for silicon is shown in Fig. 3.4. Selenium also has good transmission properties over this region and extending into the far infrared but its use is limited by poor thermal stability and it deforms above 50°C.

At longer wavelengths including the output at 10·6 μm of CO_2 lasers, the alkali halides, germanium, and gallium arsenide are extensively used and their properties

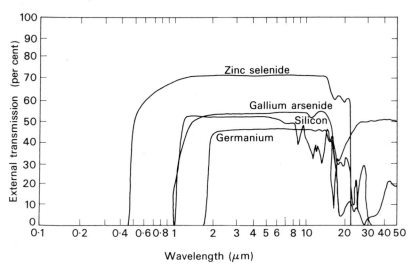

Fig. 3.4 *The external transmission of silicon, germanium, and gallium arsenide (2 mm thick)*

have been compared at medium and high power densities.[7] The alkali halides are transparent over a wide range of wavelengths in the visible and infrared region[5] and their relatively low refractive indices enable them to be used without anti-reflection coatings but they have a limited life under ambient conditions. The use of sodium chloride is limited to continuous power densities below about 1 W/mm² and stress cracks develop with use. Potassium chloride, which is capable of handling higher power densities, is often preferred.

The alkali halides are readily soluble in water. As a result they are particularly susceptible to damage by condensation of water vapour which is difficult to avoid under normal operating conditions. Due to the high solubility in water of the alkali halides the surface absorption should also be taken into account when comparing the transmission. The halides may be coated to reduce deterioration under atmospheric conditions; however, this results in increased cost and except for experimental or initial setting up trials they have been largely superseded by germanium and gallium arsenide.

The external transmission of germanium and gallium arsenide is shown in Fig. 3.4. Both are opaque in the visible region. The maximum continuous power density that can be transmitted by germanium with water cooling is limited to around 5 W/mm² due to the rapid increase in absorption that occurs with temperature at around 40°C. The absorption coefficient of gallium arsenide is lower than that of germanium but operation at higher power densities is possible, thermal runaway occurring above about 400°C. At moderate power densities (about 5×10^6 W/m²) water cooling is not necessary, though excessive thermal expansion which may cause distortion, particularly of curved components, may occur. Cadmium telluride also has good transmission properties in the infra-red, a high melting point and a thermal runaway temperature of about 200°C but is difficult to manufacture except in hot pressed crystalline form.

The high refractive index of both germanium and gallium arsenide make the use of an anti-reflection coating necessary unless a high reflectivity is required. (This is sometimes utilized when using germanium or gallium arsenide for the output window of a CO_2 laser.)

Some of the materials that have transmission characteristics that are suitable for use in the infrared region of the spectrum can be produced in suitable forms as hot pressed polycrystalline materials. The properties are only slightly different from the same material formed by other methods. The external transmission characteristics of the Irtran (Trademark Kodak Ltd) range of hot-pressed polycrystalline materials are shown in Fig. 3.5.

The properties of zinc sulphide, zinc selenide, calcium fluoride, and silicon are suitable for low-power applications but their relatively low transmission at 10·6 µm limits their application at high power. More recently zinc selenide has been produced by chemical vapour deposition which has a lower absorption coefficient (0·05/mm) than in the hot pressed polycrystalline form and is suitable for use with high power CO_2 lasers. The transmission characteristic is also shown in Fig. 3.4. Some of these materials have been used for anti-reflection coatings in the infrared region.

3.1.2 Optical interference coatings Optical interference coatings are used for increasing the transmission of lenses, windows, and prisms by reducing reflection losses and as spectral filters and for high reflectivity coatings.[8]

The reflectivity at the interface between two materials of refractive indices n_1 and

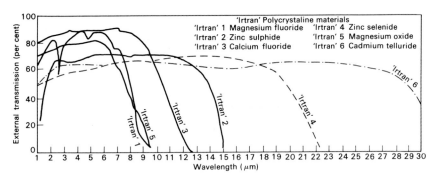

Fig. 3.5 *The external transmission of Irtran materials (2 mm thick) (courtesy Kodak Limited)*

n_2 can be reduced by using a coating of an intermediate value of refractive index n and of thickness $\lambda/4$ (quarter wavelength) at the transmission wavelength. Destructive interference occurs at the interface between the coating and its substrate. The minimum reflectivity at the interface is obtained when

$$\left(\frac{n_1 n_2 - n^2}{n_1 n_2 + n^2}\right)^2 = 0 \tag{3.5}$$

The optimum value of refractive index of the coating material is obtained when $n_1 . n_2 = n^2$ which at an interface where one of the materials is air, is obtained when $n = \sqrt{n_2}$. Reflection still occurs at the first interface with the coating material and more than one coating may be used to reduce this to a minimum. Where a suitable coating material of the required refractive index is not available more than one coat may be used.

A reflecting coating can be obtained by using alternate coatings of different refractive indexes and of thickness $\lambda/2$ (half-wave coating) so that constructive interference occurs at the interfaces between the coatings.

Broad- and narrow-band spectral filters of precise transmission characteristics can be achieved by using a combination of coatings of high reflectivity over the stop band and high transmission over the pass band.

The techniques of deposition and the properties of thin film interference coatings have been extensively studied.[9,10,11] Some materials suitable for interference coatings are summarized in table 3.2. Most of these are suitable for use over the visible and near infrared regions at moderate power densities; however, in the infrared relatively few materials are available. Coatings for use in the infrared, include lead chloride, magnesium fluoride, didymium fluoride, silicon monoxide, zinc sulphide; cerium dioxide and silicon have been measured.

Ideally the coating should have a high transmission at the required wavelength. However, since only a thin layer is required the absorption is normally negligible and a higher absorption coefficient than if the material were for use as a window or lens is often acceptable. At high power densities damage to the coating by absorption may be an important criterion affecting the choice of a coating material for a given application. Some materials that would be difficult to fabricate as free-standing optical components may be used for coatings.

Table 3.2 *Materials used for interference coatings*

Material	Refractive Index (approximate)
Aluminium oxide (Al$_2$O$_3$)	1·78
Antimony oxide (Sb$_2$O$_2$)	2·1
Antimony sulphide (Sb$_2$S$_2$)	2·8–3·0
Bismuth oxide (Bi$_2$O$_8$)	2·45
Cadmium oxide (CdO)	2·06
Cadmium sulphide (CdS)	2·26–2·5
Calcium fluoride (CaF$_2$)	1·22
Cerium dioxide (CeO$_2$)	2·2–2·4
Cerium fluoride (CeF$_3$)	1·6–1·75
Cesium bromide (CsBr)	1·9
Cryolite (3NaF.AlF$_3$)	1·35
Didymium fluoride	1·57
Gadolinium titanate (Gd$_2$O$_3$.2TiO$_2$)	2·34
Germanium (Ge)	4
Indium oxide (In$_2$O$_3$)	1·7
Lead chloride (PbCl$_2$)	2·2
Lead fluoride (PbF$_2$)	1·75–2·05
Lead telluride (PbTe)	5·1
Lithium fluoride (LiF)	1·36
Magnesium fluoride (MgF$_2$)	1·38
Neodymium trioxide (Nd$_2$O$_3$)	2·0
Silicon dioxide (SiO$_2$)	1·46
Silicon monoxide (SiO)	1·6–1·9
Silver chloride (AgCl)	2·06
Sodium chloride (NaCl)	1·5
Tellurium (Te)	5
Thorium dioxide (ThO$_2$)	1·75–1·9
Thorium fluoride (ThF$_4$)	1·45
Titanium dioxide (TiO$_2$)	2·4–2·6
Zinc sulphide (ZnS)	2·3
Zirconium dioxide (ZrO$_2$)	2·10

3.1.3 The absorption of air and water For many practical laser applications the optical path is mainly through air. The attenuation of air is dependent on the amount of water vapour present and the presence of other gases and particles. The attenuation is usually low in the visible region but increases at wavelengths below about 0·185 μm in the near ultraviolet and for efficient transmission vacuum systems are required. The transmission is high in the infrared except for selective absorption over narrow bands. The relative absorption in the infrared of the individual constituents of air normally encountered in variable concentrations (ozone, carbon dioxide, and water vapour), are shown in Fig. 3.6. A detailed treatment of atmospheric transmission for a wide variety of conditions is given by Eppers.[13]

Over the path lengths normally encountered in laser systems and laboratory and industrial applications (e.g., < 10 m) the attenuation may often be ignored but over long distances such as those used in communications, range finding, and pollution detection it is sometimes necessary to allow for atmospheric attenuation.

Over long path lengths the effect of water vapour and in particular fog and aerosols

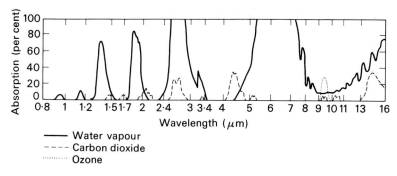

Fig. 3.6 *Distribution of absorption bands of water vapour, carbon dioxide, and ozone in the earth's atmosphere (from Vasko, A.,* Infra-Red Radiation, *Iliffe Books, London, 1968. © SNTL Prague)*

of all kinds is to cause attenuation by scattering as well as by absorption and this should also be considered. Table 3.3 indicates a typical range of distribution of particle sizes from various sources. The scattering of light by particles that are large compared with the wavelength of the light is a combination of diffraction, diffuse reflection, and refraction. The scattering effect is almost independent of wavelength unless selective absorption occurs. Where the particles themselves are small compared with the wavelength, the scattered intensity is proportional to the square of the volume of the individual particles and proportional to $1/\lambda^4$. As the particle size is reduced further the intensity of the scattered light decreases rapidly; however, effects due to scattering are still apparent at molecular dimensions and are used in some methods of analysis and pollution detection.

Water is the most commonly encountered liquid in optical systems. Used for cooling, it may also be present in hygroscopic and porous materials. The spectral transmission of distilled water is shown in Fig. 3.7[14] for various path lengths.

The absorption is low over the range $0·3\,\mu m$ to $0·8\,\mu m$ but at longer and shorter wavelengths the absorption is high. Organic solvents are also encountered in optical systems in devices such as Kerr cells and dye cells for Q switching, but the range and concentrations possible are too varied to generalize. The infrared absorption spectra of a number of common organic solvents with transmission bands over the range $3\,\mu m$ to $20\,\mu m$ have been obtained.[15]

Table 3.3 *Typical particle size distributions (from Vasko, A.,* Infra-Red Radiation, *Iliffe Books, London, 1968. © SNTL Prague)*

Source	Size Distribution
Dust	1 μm and over, but mostly greater than 10 μm
Smoke	0·001 μm–1 μm; for industrial smoke up to 100 μm
Atmospheric cloudiness	Less than 1 μm but generally 0·001 μm–0·1 μm
Fog and clouds	1 μm–100 μm
'Light' haze (mostly)	0·001 μm–0·1 μm
'Dense' haze	1 μm–10 μm
Drizzle	100 μm–400 μm
Rain	400 μm–4000 μm

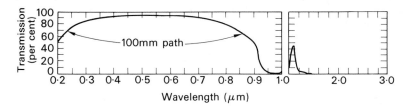

Fig. 3.7 *Spectral transmission of distilled water (courtesy Oriel Corp of America)*

3.2 Bi-refringent materials

Bi-refringence is the effect that occurs due to variation of the refractive index of a material in one or more directions. Natural bi-refringence is normally associated with crystalline materials with a non-cubic crystalline structure and a wide variety of materials exhibit some degree of bi-refringence.

A beam that is passed through a bi-refringent material becomes polarized. The amount or degree of polarization will depend on the directions of the axis of the material relative to the beam. Various kinds of polarization can occur, the most commonly encountered being circular and elliptical polarization.

The ray in the plane in which circular polarization occurs is termed the ordinary ray, the ray in the plane in which the wave-front is elliptical is termed the extraordinary ray.

Bi-refringence may be induced in some materials by various methods (e.g., electric field, pressure developed by accoustic waves, or magnetic fields) and such materials are referred to as electro-optic, accousto-optic, or magneto-optic.

The phenomenon of bi-refringence is extensively used in optical systems for deflection, switching, scanning, and modulation.

3.2.1 Polarizing Prisms The refractive index of bi-refringent materials depends on the axis along which it is measured. Since the velocity of light is inversely proportional to the refractive index, the axis of lowest refractive index is termed the fast axis, the axis with the highest refractive index the slow axis. Bi-refringent materials are

Table 3.4 *Properties of birefringent crystals measured at sodium line (from* Catalogue Optics '72. *Continental Optical Corporation)*

Material	Refractive indices		Δn	Transmission Band (μm)
	n_o	n_e		
Magnesium Fluoride, MgF_2	1·378	1·390	+0·012	0·11–6·5
Calcite, $CaCO_3$	1·658	1·486	−0·172	0·20–2·0
Crystal Quartz, SiO_2	1·544	1·553	+0·009	0·16–4·5
Sodium Nitrate, $NaNO_3$	1·585	1·336	−0·249	0·35–3·0
Rutile, TiO_2	2·616	2·903	+0·287	0·45–4·3
Cadmium Sulphide, CdS	2·334	2·352	+0·018	0·60–14·0
Sapphire, Al_2O_3	1·768	1·760	−0·008	0·17–6·0
ADP, $NH_4H_2PO_4$	1·479	1·524	+0·045	0·14–1·4
KDP, KH_2PO_4	1·510	1·468	−0·042	0·20–1·4

principally used where optical polarization by transmission is required. Polarizing prisms of bi-refringent materials are also used for beam deflection, and for polarizing the laser beam outside the laser cavity. Table 3.4 lists some of the more common bi-refringent materials together with their refractive indices measured at the sodium D line (0·59 μm). Of these, in and around the visible region, calcite ($CaCO_3$) which has a high bi-refringence and a refractive index compatible with optical cements enabling it to be used in multi-element prism construction, is most used. The bi-refringence of crystalline quartz is less than that of calcite but it is capable of transmitting high powers and is also used in the visible region. Sodium nitrate has a high bi-refringence but is hygroscopic and difficult to work, while rutile (TiO_2) has a high refractive index and hence requires coating to reduce the reflectivity to acceptable values. At long wavelengths in the infrared few materials are available and polarization by reflection is sometimes used.

A large number of different constructions of prisms exists.[16] Polarizing prisms normally comprise two prisms, selection of the polarized beam occurring by total internal reflection of one beam at the interface. The reflected beam may be absorbed in a lossy layer at a side face (single beam polarizer) or may emerge obliquely (double beam polarizer). The two components may be cemented at the interface; this, however, reduces the transmission in the ultraviolet and limits the power that can be transmitted to less than $100\,mW/mm^2$.

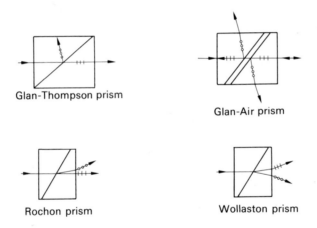

Glan-Thompson prism

Glan-Air prism

Rochon prism

Wollaston prism

Fig. 3.8 Polarizing prisms used in laser systems

Various prisms used for polarizing laser beams are shown in Fig. 3.8. The direction of polarization perpendicular to the plane of the ray is shown by dots and polarization parallel to the plane of the ray by transverse lines. The Glan-Thompson prism uses cement to bond the prisms and hence is limited in its power-handling capacity. The Glan-Air prism which is specially developed for high-power laser operation relies on partial reflection at the interface and the transmitted power is not limited by the bonding medium. Various types of the Glan-Air prism exist. The side faces of the prisms may be polished so that the unwanted beam is transmitted rather than absorbed, preventing damage at high powers and the prism is then suitable for intra-cavity laser applications. The exit face may be cut so that the unwanted beam is normal to it, minimizing back reflection. The faces may be anti-reflection coated for use at moderate power levels.

Examples of polarizing prisms in which both rays are transmitted through the same face are the Rochon and Wollaston prisms, both of which are optically cemented together and therefore limited in the power they can transmit. These are also illustrated in Fig. 3.8. The extraordinary ray is transmitted undeviated through the Rochon prism at all wavelengths, while the ordinary ray is undeviated in a Senarmont prism. Both rays are deviated at the interface in the Wollaston prism enabling a greater separation between the two rays to be obtained.

3.2.2 Wave-retardation plates Wave-retardation plates, also referred to as retarder wave plates and phase shifters, are used to change the direction of polarization of polarized light without changing the degree of polarization or intensity of the light.

A linear retarder usually has two orthogonal axes perpendicular to the transmission axis corresponding to the fast and slow axes. The refractive index of the slow axis is greater than that of the fast axis. Light polarized along either of these axes will be transmitted with its polarization form unchanged. Light polarized in a direction between the two axes will be resolved into fast and slow components which re-combine so that the emerging beam has a different form of polarization to the incident beam. The phase shift is the amount by which the component on the slow axis is retarded with respect to that on the fast axis. Materials normally used are crystalline quartz cut parallel to the optic axis and sheet mica.

The retardation (phase shift) is directly proportional to the thickness of the plate and inversely proportional to the wavelength of the incident light. 90° phase shift (quarter-wave plate) converts linearly polarized light into circularly or elliptically polarized light (and vice versa). 180° phase shift (half-wave plate) converts linear polarization forms to symmetrical with respect to its own axis, right circularly polarized light to left circularly polarized light, and right elliptically polarized light to left elliptically polarized light. The half-wave plate will also convert the major axis of the ellipse symmetrically about the plate's own fast axis.

3.2.3 Electro-optic bi-refringent materials Bi-refringence is induced in some materials in an electric field.[17] Many optical materials exhibit some degree of electro-optically induced bi-refringence.[18, 19] Electro-optically induced bi-refringence may be used for Q switching, scanning, modulation, and frequency conversion of the output of lasers.

The properties of electro-optic bi-refringent materials may be divided into optical properties and electrical properties. Important optical properties include:

(a) The optical quality of the material.
(b) The degree of bi-refringence induced by the electro-optic effect.
(c) The optical absorption which limits the range of transmission.
(d) The refractive index which governs the velocity of light in the material and the reflection losses at the faces.
(e) Damage threshold.

Important electrical properties are:

(a) The relative permittivity which effects the capacitance and hence the maximum modulating frequency.

(b) The dielectric loss which limits the electrical power dissipation at high frequencies in the crystal when a.c. modulation is used.

Electro-optic devices can be used for beam deflection, Q switching, amplitude or phase modulation, and parametric oscillators.

The two most commonly used electro-optic effects are the quadratic or Kerr effect and the linear Pockels effect.[19]

The Kerr effect uses the variation in refractive index that can be induced in the plane of a transverse electric field. The induced bi-refringence is given by

$$\Delta n = BlE^2 \tag{3.6}$$

where Δn is the induced bi-refringence, l the path length and B is the Kerr constant.

Table 3.5 Kerr's constant for typical liquids (from Coherent Light, Harvey, A. F., Copyright © 1970, John Wiley & Sons Ltd. By permission John Wiley & Sons Ltd)

Liquid	B at 20°C and 0·59 μm	n_{ro} (optical)	ε_r (h.f.)
	(μm/V²)		
Nitrobenzene	0·044	1·55	36
Nitrotoluene	0·013 700	1·55	
Acetone	0·001 800	1·36	21
Chlorobenzene	0·001 100	1·52	5·9
Water	0·000 520	1·33	20–80
Chloroform	−0·000 370	1·45	5·1
Carbon disulphide	0·000 360	1·63	2·64
Benzene	0·000 070	1·51	2·28

The Kerr constant for various materials is listed in table 3.5.[19] The transmission bands of suitable liquids and solids are limited to around the visible region. Nitrobenzene, which is polar and has a high Kerr constant, is frequently used and typically requires an operating voltage of about 30 kV. Non-polar liquids have the highest rate of response which can be of the order of 10^{-11} s.

Kerr cells can be used together with polarizing plates for Q switching and amplitude or phase modulation (Fig. 3.9). The material of the cell has to be considered in the design of optical systems and anti-reflection coating may be required in low loss systems. Kerr cells have generally been superseded by Pockels cells and other devices enabling lower operating voltages to be used.

The Pockels effect is a linear effect. The operating voltage is lower than that of a Kerr cell, typically of the order of 100 V to 10 kV, depending on the direction of the applied electric field. The induced bi-refringence

$$\Delta n = n^2 E_r \tag{3.7}$$

where E_r is the electro-optic coefficient and is dependent on the orientation of the crystal.

The use of Pockels cells is limited to highly collimated light in very close alignment to the optical axis; however, this is normally readily obtained with lasers. The Kerr

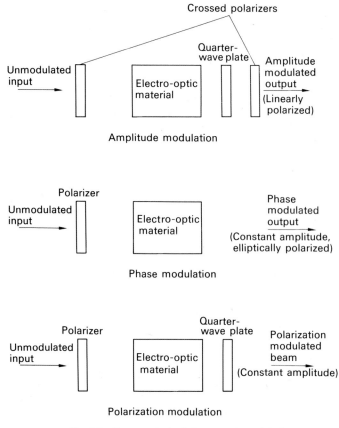

Fig. 3.9   *Some methods of electro-optic modulation*

cell is less directionally sensitive. Pockels cells are, however, capable of operating at lower voltages with a faster response than Kerr cells and use solid non-toxic materials.

Pockels cells can be used for modulation and related applications. Some examples of their use for various forms of modulation are shown in Fig. 3.9. Plane polarized light can also be elliptically polarized in this way, the intensity of polarization being proportional to the electric field.

A wide variety of optical materials exhibit some degree of electro-optic properties.[18] The properties of some of the principal linear electro-optic materials that are used are listed in table 3.6. Most of these are commercially available in electro-optic devices. The properties are normally anisotropic and it is therefore difficult to specify values without reference to the crystal axis. For purposes of comparison the limits of variation in refractive index together with the maximum reported value of electro-optic coefficient and the half-wave voltage (where applicable) are given. The transmission band corresponds to the limits of external transmission at long and short wavelengths for a sample 2 mm thick at which the transmittance is 10 per cent. Selective absorption may also occur over narrow bands within the transmission band. ADP and KDP, RDP and CDP type crystals are also obtainable as their deuterated isomorphs A*DP, K*DP and R*DP in which a deuterium molecule replaces the hydrogen molecule.

Table 3.6 *Electro-optic properties of optical materials used in laser systems*

	Refractive index	Electro-optic constant (10^{-12}m/V)	Half-wave voltage (kV)	Transmission Band (μm) 0·1 0·5 1 5 10 50
Ammonium dihydrogen arsenate* (ADA), $NH_4H_2AsO_4$	1·52	9·2	7	
Ammonium dihydrogen phosphate* (ADP), $NH_4H_2PO_4$	1·48–1·53	24·5	9	
Barium sodium niobate, $Ba_2NaNb_5O_{15}$	2·22–2·32	92		
Cadmium telluride, CdTe	2·6	6·8		
Cesium dihydrogen arsenate (CDA), CsH_2AsO_4	1·56	18·6	3	
Gallium arsenide, GaAs	3·3–3·6	12·0		
Lithium formate monohydrate, $LiCHO_2.H_2O$	1·36–1·52			
Lithium iodate, LiO_3	1·74–1·88	6·4		
Lithium niobate, $LiNbO_3$	2·06–2·38	32·2	2	
Lithium tantalate, $LiTaO_3$	2·03–2·18	30·3		
Potassium dihydrogen arsenate* (KDA), KH_2AsO_4	1·52–1·57	12·5	6	
Potassium dihydrogen phosphate* (KDP), KH_2PO_4	1·47–1·51	10·5	7	
Proustite Ag_3AsS_3	2·59–2·83	2·78	—	
Rubidium dihydrogen arsenate* (RDA), RbH_2AsO_4	1·52–1·56	13·0	4	
Rubidium dihydrogen phosphate* (RDP), RbH_2PO_4	1·5	15·5		

0·1   0·5   1   5   10   50

*Also available as deuterated isomorphs.

These forms have essentially similar characteristics with cut-off occurring at rather longer wavelengths in the infrared and lower halfwave voltages. For more specific details the reader is referred to reference 18 and to manufacturers' data.

KDP and ADP have been extensively investigated and their external transmission characteristics are shown in Fig. 3.10.

The direction of the applied electric field is dependent on the relative direction of the optic and electric axes of the crystal. If the electric axis is perpendicular to the optic axis the electric field is applied transverse to the optic axis and it is referred to as a transverse modulator. If the axes coincide the electrodes are placed at either end of the crystal which is normally in the form of a long thin parallelepiped. Transparent conducting electrode or mesh or grid electrodes are used, and it is referred to as a longitudinal modulator.

The voltage sensitivity is given by the half-wave voltage required to rotate the polarizing plane through 90°, producing 100 per cent modulation. For longitudinal modulators the half-wave voltage normally varies from 1·5 kV to 20·0 kV and for transverse modulators the half-wave voltage varies from 100 V to 1000 V depending on the material used. The voltage sensitivity of longitudinal modulators can be increased by connecting them optically in series and electrically in parallel and the large linear

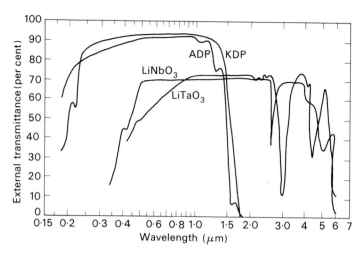

Fig. 3.10 *External transmission of ADP, KDP, lithium iodate, lithium niobate and lithium tantalate*

and angular aperture possible allows them to be used with lasers and conventional light sources.

The high sensitivity of transverse modulators enables them to be used at low voltages, and voltage biasing the crystals to the linear region is normally used. The electrodes of transverse modulation crystals are, however, temperature sensitive and operation in a controlled oven may be necessary. Contrast ratios are normally an order of magnitude less than obtainable with longitudinal modulators.

A change in refractive index induced by an electric field of 2 kV/mm in a material with an electro-optic constant of 10^{-11} m/V, corresponds to a difference of only about 0·05 per cent between the relative speeds on the two axes and hence refractive indices in the two planes. If the extraordinary ray is retarded through $\frac{1}{2}$ wavelength (180°) the plane of polarization of the resultant of the ordinary and extraordinary rays is rotated by 90°. By rotating the plane of polarization in conjunction with a polarizer, varying degrees of modulation can be achieved.

The relative transmittance is given by

$$T = \frac{I_{\text{out}}}{I_{\text{in}}} = T_{\text{max}} \sin^2 \phi$$

where
$$\phi = (2\pi/\lambda)n_0^3 \, E_r V \qquad (3.8)$$

and where V is the applied voltage.

By inserting a quarter-wave plate the output is brought to a quasi-linear region of the characteristic and approximately linear modulation is obtainable over the range ± 10 per cent V about this point. Alternatively a bias voltage, typically of 0·4 kV, may be applied to the crystal to bring the operating point to a linear part of the characteristic corresponding to $V_{\text{max}}/2$. Changes in refractive index Δn of the order of 5×10^{-3} are obtainable with barium titanate and potassium tantalum niobate (KTN); however, the optical quality of other materials such as KDP ($\Delta n = 10^{-4}$) is superior.

ADP, KDP, and K*DP are used as longitudinal modulators with the electric field parallel to the optic axis. The half-wave voltage required by K*DP is less than KDP which in turn is less than ADP. One application is for Q switching for which the jitter (variation in delay between firing and emission of the laser pulse) is less than that of dye cells and the pulse-to-pulse stability is also within 10 per cent. A high power Q switch using K*DP with less than $\frac{1}{2}$ per cent insertion loss and capable of working peak power of 2 MW/mm^2 has been described.[20] Modulation and frequency doubling are possible but damage also occurs at high powers. ADP, KDP, and K*DP are hygroscopic and are normally mounted in a cell containing a dielectric fluid with anti-reflection coated windows and with suitable optical and electrical properties. Other materials with similar properties include potassium dihydrogen arsenate, rubidium dihydrogen arsenate, cesium dihydrogen arsenate, and ammonium dihydrogen arsenate and their deuterated isomorphs.

Materials with transverse modulation characteristics such as lithium niobate and lithium tantalate can also be used for Q switching and modulation. The relative electro-optic coefficients of KDP, ADP, LiNbO$_3$, and α-HIO$_3$ have been measured.[21]

Destruction thresholds for ADP, KDP, and LiNbO$_3$ have been measured at 0·53 μm and 1·06 μm.[22] The threshold level was found to be dependent on wavelength and focal length of focusing lens and was higher for long focal length lenses for which the depth of focus was longer. The destruction threshold was highest for ADP but in all cases was above 10^7 MW/m^2.

The non-linear electro-optic effect in crystals is also used for second harmonic generation and in parametric amplifiers and oscillators.[17] The properties of non-linear optic materials and their second harmonic coefficients has been surveyed.[23]

Second harmonic generation is most frequently used for converting the output wavelengths of YAG and ruby lasers to shorter wavelengths at efficiencies in excess of 40 per cent. Second harmonic generation at 0·347 μm from the output of ruby lasers at 40 per cent efficiency has been reported using LiIO$_3$ and LiNbO$_3$.[24] LiIO$_3$ and LiNbO$_3$ have been used for intra-cavity second harmonic generation at 0·53 μm from the output of a neodymium–YAG laser.[25] LiIO$_3$ is reported to be best for Q-switched operation due to its higher resistance to surface damage but LiNbO$_3$ is preferable for CW operation because of its greater non-linearity and its angularly insensitive phase matching. Lithium formate monohydrate has also been used for doubling the output of ruby and YAG lasers at high power densities. Higher harmonics can be achieved by having more than one stage of second harmonic generation. At 10·6 μm proustite (Ag$_3$AsS$_3$) has been used to obtain the second harmonic at 5·3 μm.

The second harmonic frequency is generated by the interaction of the ordinary and extraordinary waves in a bi-refringent crystal. The second harmonic power P_2 is given by

$$P_2 = \frac{P_1^2 l^2 d_s \sin^2 \theta}{2\pi f_0}$$

where P_1 is the fundamental power, l the crystal length, d_s is the SHG coefficient, θ is the angle between the optic axis of the crystal and the fundamental beam under phase matched conditions, and f_0 is the fundamental frequency.

Phase matching can be achieved by using the bi-refringence to cancel out the effects of dispersion in the crystal. This is obtained when the angle between the beam and the optic axis is chosen correctly. The highest conversion efficiency is obtained when the phase matching angle is 90° to the optic axis of the crystal. This condition is not normally encountered with crystals of naturally occurring bi-refringence but can be achieved with some electro-optic materials by applying a d.c. electric field to bias the crystal and by maintaining it at a constant temperature.

Parametric frequency conversion combines two beams of different frequencies but comparable intensities in a non-linear optical material to produce a third frequency equal to the sum or difference of the other two frequencies.[17,26] The efficiencies of conversion are normally much lower than obtainable by second harmonic conversion in a crystal; however, the output is tunable and can also be used to generate sub-harmonic frequencies. Up to now, however, parametric frequency conversion has found little application.

3.2.4 Magneto-optic materials Various forms of magneto-optic deflection exist[19] of which the Faraday effect is typical. The angle of deflection is given by

$$\theta = VHl \tag{3.9}$$

where θ is the angle of deflection, V is Verdet's constant, H is the magnetic field strength and l is the optical path length.

Typical values for Verdet's constant for glasses are of the order of 10 rad/T m for diamagnetic glasses but may be over 1000 rad/T m for paramagnetic glasses.[19] The values vary with glass composition and wavelength.

The direction of rotation is considered positive when it is clockwise, negative when anti-clockwise. Considerable enhancement of the effect can be obtained by increasing the path length by allowing multiple reflections to occur. The deflection of a laser beam by the Faraday effect has been used for the remote measurement of electric currents at high voltages.

3.2.5 Acousto-optic materials Acoustic vibrations in a transmitting medium give rise to local variations in refractive index.[17,27] If a suitable standing wave is set up in the material such as by a piezo-electric transducer a change in refractive index occurs in the plane transverse to the acoustic wave and the extraordinary ray is deflected as shown in Fig. 3.11. Alternatively the oscillating variations in the refractive index may be used to provide a method of scanning the beam.

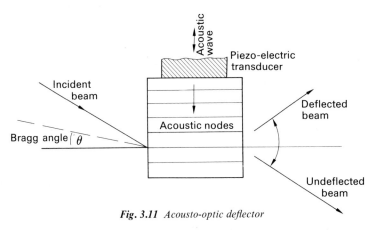

Fig. 3.11 Acousto-optic deflector

44

Light waves passing through the crystal approximately parallel to the acoustic wave fronts are diffracted by the acoustic wave fronts which act in a similar way to a phase grating. If the light strikes the grating formed in this way the light is deflected at the Bragg angle in the same way as X-rays are reflected by lattice planes in a crystal. Under the correct conditions nearly 100 per cent of the incident light can be deflected in this way.

The angle between the undeflected and deflected beam is given by

$$\sin \theta = \frac{\lambda_0}{\lambda_s} \tag{3.10}$$

where λ_0 is the wavelength of incident light and λ_s is the wavelength of acoustic wave.

The total deviation possible for an acoustic bandwidth $\Delta\lambda_s$ is

$$\Delta\phi = \frac{\lambda_0}{\Delta\lambda_s} \tag{3.11}$$

Intensity modulation is also possible since by putting a suitable aperture after the deflected beam, the intensity output will vary with the deflection. The intensity modulation is given by

$$\frac{I}{I_0} = \sin^2 \frac{\pi}{2}\left(\frac{P}{P_0}\right)^{\frac{1}{2}} \tag{3.12}$$

where I is the intensity, I_0 is the maximum intensity, P the input power and P_0 the input power at maximum deflection.

The modulation equation can be rewritten in a form similar to the equation used for electro-optic devices

$$\frac{I}{I_0} = \sin^2 \gamma V \tag{3.13}$$

where γ is a constant and V is the intensity of the acoustic signal.

Acousto-optic materials enable scanning, Q switching, mode-locking, and modulation of a laser beam to be carried out. Acousto-optic Q switches with response times of less than 1 µs with insertion losses of about 30 per cent have been developed capable of repetitive operation. They have also been used for tuning dye lasers.

A variety of materials exhibit the acousto-optic effect in which the refractive index varies with pressure. Pressure variations can be induced at high frequencies by the piezo-electric effect in materials such as barium titanate which has a high piezo-electric constant of the order of 16×10^{-11} C/N along the d_{33} axis.

The acousto-optic properties of various transmitting materials are listed for comparison in table 3.7.[28] The transmission characteristics of most of these materials are shown in table 3.1 and table 3.6.

Fused silica and glass are often used in the visible and near infrared region. New materials such as alpha-iodic acid (α-HIO$_3$) and lead molybdate (PbMoO$_4$) have also been recently developed and have potentially useful properties. At 10·6 µm only a limited range of materials are suitable for acousto-optic deflection and include germanium, gallium arsenide, and cadmium telluride. Their acousto-optic properties have been compared, together with their electro-optic properties.[29]

Table 3.7 *Figures of merit for acousto-optic materials[a] (from Dixon, R. W., 'Photoelastic Properties of Selected Materials and Their Relevance for Applications to Acoustic Light Modulators and Scanners', J. Appl. Phys., **38** (13), 5149–5258, 1967)*

Material	$\lambda(\mu)$	n	$\rho(g/cm^3)$	Acoustic wave polarization and direction	$u(10^5 cm/s)$	Opt. wave polarization and direction[a]	$M_1(n^7p^2/\rho U)^c$ $\times 10^7$	$M_2(n^6p^2/\rho U^3)$ $\times 10^{18}$	$M_3(n^7p^2/\rho U^2)$ $\times 10^{12}$	P_a/f_o (mW/MHz)
Fused quartz	0·63	1·46	2·2	long.	5·95	$\perp$	7·89	1·51	1·29	5·4
Fused quartz	0·63			trans.	3·76	$\parallel$ or $\perp$	0·963	0·467	0·256	27·1
GaP	0·63	3·31	4·13	long. in [110]	6·32	$\parallel$	590	44·6	93·5	0·074
GaP	0·63			trans. in [100]	4·13	$\parallel$ or $\perp$ in [010]	137	24·1	33·1	0·21
GaAs	1·15	3·37	5·34	long. in [110]	5·15	$\parallel$	925	104	179	0·24
GaAs	1·15			trans. in [100]	3·32	$\parallel$ or $\perp$ in [010]	155	46·3	49·2	0·86
TiO$_2$	0·63	2·58	4·6	long. in [11–20]	7·86	$\perp$ in [001]	62·5	3·93	7·97	0·87
LiNbO$_3$	0·63	2·20	4·7	long. in [11–20]	6·57	(b)	66·5	6·99	10·1	0·69
YAG	0·63	1·83	4·2	long. in [100]	8·53	$\parallel$	0·16	0·012	0·019	370
YAG	0·63			long. in [110]	8·60	$\perp$	0·98	0·073	0·114	61
YIG	1·15	2·22	5·17	long. in [100]	7·21	$\perp$	3·94	0·33	0·53	80
LiTaO$_3$	0·63	2·18	7·45	long. in [001]	6·19	$\parallel$	11·4	1·37	1·84	3·8
As$_2$S$_3$	0·63	2·61	3·20	long.	2·6	$\perp$	762	433	293	0·024
As$_2$S$_3$	1·15	2·46		long.		$\parallel$	619	347	236	0·179
SF-4	0·63	1·616	3·59	long.	3·63	$\perp$	1·83	4·51	3·97	1·75
β-ZnS	0·63	2·35	4·10	long. in [110]	5·51	$\parallel$ in [001]	24·3	3·41	4·41	1·58
β-ZnS	0·63			trans. in [110]	2·165	$\parallel$ or $\perp$ in [001]	10·6	0·57	4·9	1·42
α-Al$_2$O$_3$	0·63	1·76	4·0	long. in [001]	11·15	$\parallel$ in [11–20]	7·32	0·34	0·66	10·5
CdS	0·63	2·44	4·82	long. in [11–20]	4·17	$\parallel$	51·8	12·1	12·4	0·56
ADP	0·63	1·58	1·803	long. in [100]	6·15	$\parallel$ in [010]	16·0	2·78	2·62	2·65
ADP	0·63			trans. in [100]	1·83	$\parallel$ or $\perp$ in [001]	3·34	6·43	1·83	3·8
KDP	0·63	1·51	2·34	long. in [100]	5·50	$\parallel$ in [010]	8·72	1·91	1·45	4·8
KDP	0·63			trans. in [100]		$\parallel$ or $\perp$ in [001]	1·57	3·83	0·95	7·3
H$_2$O	0·63	1·33	1·0	long.	1·5		43·6	160	29·1	0·24
Te[b]	10·6	4·8	6·24	long. in [11–20]	2·2	$\parallel$ in [0001]	10200	4400	4640	7·14

[a] The optical-beam direction actually differs from that indicated by the magnitude of the Bragg angle. The polarization is defined as parallel or perpendicular to the scattering plane formed by the acoustic and optical k-vectors.
[b] An ordinarily polarized wave is assumed. If the increased optical absorption (due to impurities in the currently available samples) of the extraordinary polarization can be tolerated, then $M_1 = 5.7 \times 10^{-3}$. $M_2 = 2.02 \times 10^{-14}$, $M_3 = 2.59 \times 10^{-8}$, and $P_a/f_o = 1.28$ mW/MHz.
[c] Figures of merit are given in cgs units.

The acousto-optic properties of materials may be assessed by various criteria and the properties of many materials have been measured. These are tabulated in table 3.7 in terms of the figure of merit M_1 where

$$M_1 = \frac{n^7 p^2}{\rho U^3} \tag{3.14}$$

where ρ is the density, p is the pressure, and U is the velocity of the soundwave in the material. The relation M_1 is of importance where both bandwidth and intensity of the diffracted beam are important.

If only the light intensity is important then

$$M_2 = \frac{n^6 p^2}{\rho U^3} \tag{3.15}$$

which is a measure of the fraction of the incident energy scattered by an acoustic beam.

Where the acoustic beam height is not otherwise constrained and may be made as small as the height of the optical beam in the region of interaction

$$M_3 = \frac{n^7 p^2}{\rho U^2}. \tag{3.16}$$

The application of some of these materials with high values is limited by the form in which they are available, their absorption coefficient, and other properties.

3.3 Reflectors

Polished metals have a high reflectivity at infrared wavelengths and are extensively used for front surface reflectors. Metal coatings on polished substrates (which may be of a different material from the coating) with properties more suitable for optical polishing so that a higher reflectivity may be obtained, are used. The reflectivities of the most important evaporated metal coatings used for reflectors are tabulated in table 3.8 as a function of wavelength.[11, 30]

The reflectivity of aluminium is highest in the ultraviolet region of the spectrum

Table 3.8 *Per cent normal-incidence reflectance of freshly evaporated mirror coatings of aluminium, silver, gold, copper, rhodium, and platinum, from the ultraviolet to the infrared* (from Hass, G.,* Mirror Coatings, Applied Optics and Optical Engineering, *Ed. R. Kingslake, Vol. 3, Academic Press, 1965)*

$\lambda(\mu m)$	Al	Ag	Au	Cu	Rh	Pt
0·220	91·5	28·0	27·5	40·4	57·8	40·5
0·240	91·9	29·5	31·6	39·0	63·2	46·9
0·260	92·2	29·2	35·6	35·5	67·7	51·5
0·280	92·3	25·2	37·8	33·0	70·7	54·9
0·300	92·3	17·6	37·7	33·6	73·4	57·6
0·315	92·4	5·5	37·3	35·5	75·0	59·4
0·320	92·4	8·9	37·1	36·3	75·5	60·0
0·340	92·5	72·9	36·1	38·5	76·9	62·0
0·360	92·5	88·2	36·3	41·5	78·0	63·4
0·380	92·5	92·8	37·8	44·5	78·1	64·9
0·400	92·4	95·6	38·7	47·5	77·4	66·3
0·450	92·2	97·1	38·7	55·2	76·0	69·1
0·500	91·8	97·9	47·7	60·0	76·6	71·4
0·550	91·5	98·3	81·7	66·9	78·2	73·4
0·600	91·1	98·6	91·9	93·3	79·7	75·2
0·650	90·5	98·8	95·5	96·6	81·1	76·4
0·700	89·7	98·9	97·0	97·5	82·0	77·2
0·750	88·6	99·1	97·4	97·9	82·6	77·9
0·800	86·7	99·2	98·0	98·1	83·1	78·5
0·850	86·7	99·2	98·2	98·3	83·4	79·5
0·900	89·1	99·3	98·4	98·4	83·6	80·5
0·950	92·4	99·3	98·5	98·4	83·9	80·6
1·0	94·0	99·4	98·6	98·5	84·2	80·7
1·5	97·4	99·4	99·0	98·5	87·7	81·8
2·0	97·8	99·4	99·1	98·6	91·4	81·8
3·0	98·0	99·4	99·3	98·6	95·0	90·6
4·0	98·2	99·4	99·4	98·7	95·8	93·7
5·0	98·4	99·5	99·4	98·7	96·4	94·9
6·0	98·5	99·5	99·4	98·7	96·8	95·6
7·0	98·6	99·5	99·4	98·7	97·0	95·9
8·0	98·7	99·5	99·4	98·8	97·2	96·0
9·0	98·7	99·5	99·4	98·8	97·4	96·1
10·0	98·7	99·5	99·4	98·9	97·6	96·2
15·0	98·9	99·6	99·4	99·0	98·1	96·5
20·0	99·0	99·6	99·4			
30·0	99·2	99·6	99·4			

*The reflectance of a good evaporated mirror coating is always higher than that of a polished or electroplated surface of the same material.

and higher reflectivities can only be achieved with dielectric coatings. A thin oxide layer about 3×10^{-9} m thick, which has a negligible effect on the reflectivity forms and protects the aluminium. Over the visible region the reflectivity of silver is higher than that of aluminium but it tends to tarnish when unprotected. In the near infrared, silver, gold, and copper have higher reflectivities than aluminium, however, copper also tends to tarnish under atmospheric conditions. In the middle infrared the reflectivity of gold is highest and it does not tarnish. The reflectivity of platinum and rhodium is lower than for the other materials over most of the range; however, their coatings are very durable and they can be used under very adverse conditions.

Removal of the oxide film on aluminium can occur during cleaning. Silicon monoxide (SiO) can be used to provide a hard protective coating for applications in the visible and near infrared. Magnesium fluoride (MgF_2) is used in the ultraviolet.

At low power densities where the effect of expansion is small, glasses with low co-efficients of expansion such as boro-silicate glass and fused quartz which can be worked to a highly polished surface on which a coating can be readily evaporated, are extensively used as substrates for mirrors. At higher power densities it is necessary to use a substrate of high thermal conductivity to prevent non-uniform expansion. Copper and copper alloys, notably zirconium copper, which can be more easily worked and finished are used. An improved substrate surface can be achieved by the use of an intermediate chemically deposited coating such as Kanigen (NiP_3). [Kanigen is the registered trademark of the General American Transportation Corporation.] Power densities in excess of $10\,W/mm^2$ can be sustained.

The tolerances on the dimensions of mirrors and the surface finish required is to some extent dependent on their application. Normally where it is required in a laser cavity or for focusing the beam, a similar tolerance to that required for lenses is necessary. For coated or uncoated mirrors the surface finish of the substrate is critical and should normally be smooth to within $\lambda/20$. If a coating is used the coefficient of expansion of the substrate should be as low as possible but should also be comparable with that of the coating so that it adheres securely to it. Cooling is seldom necessary except at high continuous powers such as those obtained with CO_2 lasers above about $500\,W$; however, when it is required care should be taken to avoid thermal gradients resulting in distortion of the mirror.

3.3.1 Laser mirrors

Various mirror configurations are used for laser cavities. Several different combinations of mirror geometries are illustrated in Fig. 3.12 The choice of configuration depends on the stability and acceptable beam divergence as well as efficiency. The plane-parallel combination is extremely sensitive to adjustment and variations in operating parameters but is commonly used in pulsed lasers where stability requirements are often less and where a low divergence output is required.

The long radius mirror configuration results in a beam diameter comparable with the tube diameter but with a considerably increased level of stability and the cavity volume is efficiently used. The confocal mirror system enables a higher level of stability to be achieved at the expense of reducing the useful volume in the cavity. This is extended in the case of the hemispherical mirrors which also assist lowest order mode operation in a tube of large diameter compared with the length. Various modifications of these systems are possible, improving some properties normally at the expense of others.

Unstable resonators in which one mirror is convex and the other plane or convex can be used where the gain of the cavity is adequate. Multiple reflection results in a reflected beam traversing the cavity.

The substrates for mirrors used at high continuous powers are required to dissipate the losses at the mirror without a large temperature gradient being produced which would distort the mirror. The requirements for totally reflecting mirrors are less exacting than those for partially reflecting windows. Some of the materials that are used are copper alloys, brass, vacuum-cast stainless steel, sapphire, and silica. The effectiveness of the mirror depends on the surface finish that can be achieved on the substrate which should be polished to within about 1/20 of the wavelength at which it

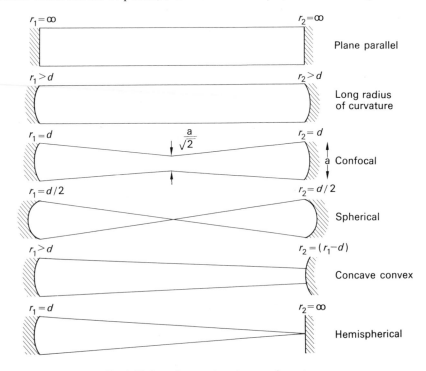

Fig. 3.12 *Some laser cavity mirror configurations*

is to be used. Fused silica and sapphire and stainless steel can be polished to very high optical finishes but are limited in their power-handling capabilities by thermal distortion. At high powers beryllium or zirconium copper can be used. High continuous powers ($>1\,\text{kW}$) may require the use of water-cooled substrates of oxygen-free high-purity copper but this is more difficult to work optically than beryllium or zirconium copper.

The output window of a laser can be regarded as a lens and the divergence can be determined if the geometry and material are known.[31] The divergence will be a minimum for a window with plane surfaces. Where a laser is designed for a specific application the lens effect can be increased by using a spherical outer surface and a combined lens and window may be used offering considerable savings both in the reduction in components and mechanical complexity but of course reducing the versatility. The growing use of lasers for specific application is likely to extend this trend further.

Although partially transmitting evaporated metal coatings may be used on a suitable transmitting substrate for the output window, the losses are high. If the gain in the laser cavity is sufficient the reflection from the uncoated surfaces of the window can be used particularly where the window has a high refractive index. Reflection from the first and second surface can be used to provide some degree of mode selection. An alternative method useful for very high powers is the hole coupled cavity in which the centre of the output window is left uncoated, the surrounding region being coated with a high reflectivity coating.

Multi-layer dielectric coatings (see section 3.2) are used at the ultraviolet end of the spectrum and the visible region where reflectivities of greater than 98 per cent over a limited bandwidth at moderate CW or pulsed powers are required. At very high powers, for example those obtained with Q-switched or mode-locked lasers, uncoated optics in the Fabry–Perot interferometer or etalon configuration shown in Fig. 3.13

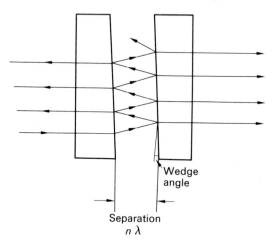

Fig. 3.13 *Fabry–Perot interferometer*

are used so as to form a resonant reflector. Resonant reflectors can also be used to improve the coherence length of the output of lasers by mode selection. Reflection occurs from both surfaces which are accurately ground so as to be parallel to within a fraction of a wavelength. Multiple reflection occurs at the interfaces which are precisely spaced so that the reflected light at each interface interferes constructively at the selected wavelength. High reflectivities not limited by the relatively low damage threshold of optically coated components can be obtained in this way.

The absorption of partially transmitting metallic coatings is normally unacceptably high and non-metallic multi-layer dielectric coatings are used for output windows and other partially reflecting surfaces. Where the gain of the laser is sufficient and the refractive index of the output window is high, the reflectivity of an uncoated window may be sufficient by itself to sustain laser action.

Reflection at the interface between two materials of different refractive indices can be used to polarize a beam of light. The maximum degree of polarization is achieved when the incident angle of the beam is at the Brewster angle which is dependent on the refractive indices of the materials at the interface. For an air–glass interface the Brewster angle is 57·5°. This is used in lasers to obtain a polarized light output or to minimize reflection at the end faces of the cavity in the plane of polarization when external mirrors are used.

At long wavelengths polarization using a reflecting grid on a transmitting substrate is possible and can be used where alternative polarizing materials are not available. Light with the plane of polarization with the electric field vector parallel to the grid is almost completely reflected; light with the plane of polarization perpendicular to the grid is mainly transmitted although some absorption occurs.

Methods of adjustment are normally by x and y planes based on a three-point kinematic support with mounting points forming an equilateral triangle and enabling adjustment in x and y planes to be made.[32] Differential screws in which one turn of the screw corresponds to only a fraction of a turn total movement may be used for precise alignment.

Final remote and very precise adjustment of optical alignment may be made using piezo-electric devices in conjunction with mechanical coarse adjustment. A typical maximum deflection of 6 μm together with an accuracy of resolution of 40×10^4 μm is possible. Piezo-electric crystals may also be used for remote axial precision deflection of optical components of 60 μm and have been used for precise tuning of lasers.

3.3.2 External reflectors Various forms of reflectors are used in laser systems. First surface plane reflectors are frequently used for changing the direction of the beam using thin film evaporated metal coatings on a polished substrate. Concave and convex mirrors are used for focusing and expanding laser beams for various applications. Off-axis parabolic mirrors are used for focusing where the power levels are too high for focusing with a lens.

A number of prisms have been developed for the deflection and reflection of beams of light.[33] Various reflecting prisms used in laser systems are shown in Fig. 3.14. The

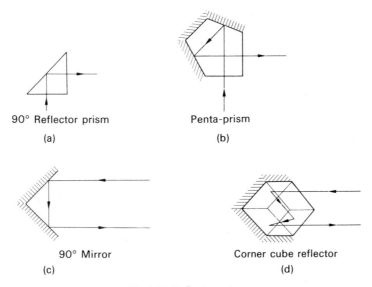

90° Reflector prism

(a)

Penta-prism

(b)

90° Mirror

(c)

Corner cube reflector

(d)

Fig. 3.14 *Reflecting prisms*

45° prism which uses an external reflective coating on one face deflects a beam by 90°. The penta-prism also deflects the incident beam through 90° but is relatively insensitive to the orientation of the beam. Three of the surfaces of the prism have reflective coatings.

Retroreflectors are used to turn the incident beam through 180° and displace it. A 90° prism with externally reflecting surfaces can be used to return a reflected ray parallel but displaced to the incident ray. At wavelengths where suitable prism materials are not available a hollow prism with internally reflecting surfaces, sometimes referred to as a roof-top reflector, may be used, and is shown in Fig. 3.14(c). The reflected ray is reflected parallel and displaced from the incident ray and is independent of variations in position about the axis up to nearly $\pm 45°$ since the change in the angle of incidence at the first mirror is compensated for by the change in the incident angle at the second mirror. Movement about any other axis will result in deflection of the reflected ray.

A cube corner prism utilizes reflection from three perpendicular faces arranged so as to form the corner of a cube angled so that the direction of the reflected ray is independent of rotation about any axis of the prism up to $\pm 35°$. A hollow cube using first surface reflection from the inside surfaces can be used. Both rooftop and the corner cube reflectors are used in folded tube lasers.

Partially reflecting dielectric coatings or diffraction gratings can be used as beam splitters. The relative magnitudes of the reflected and transmitted beams are highly dependent on the angle of incidence. Where dielectric coatings are used the reflection losses can be made less than 0·5 per cent. Low-loss partially reflecting dielectric coatings are used on the front surface and anti-reflection coatings on the back surface of the beam splitter. The substrate may be parallel but a wedge-shaped substrate results in off-axis deviation of the second reflection at the second surface. Achromatic and monochromatic coatings may be used. The direction of polarization of the beam is important where dielectric-coated beam splitters are used. The beam splitter is normally mounted at an angle of 45° to the incident beam which results in substantial polarization of unpolarized light and where linearly polarized light is used the reflectance and transmittance will vary as the plane of polarization is rotated.

Pellicle beam splitters use plastic film a few micrometres thick. The film thickness is such that effects due to second surface reflection are negligible. The film may be coated with a dielectric coating if required. A partially reflected beam may be obtained using the reflectivity that occurs at the interface at which a change in refractive index occurs.

Methods of adjustment of external mirrors are essentially the same as those used for mirrors within the laser cavity, however, the degree of precision required is often less.

3.4 Lenses

Various lenses are used in laser systems. Spherical surface optics are normally used and the design is simplified since the light is often monochromatic and the divergence of the input beam is small, and a narrow aperture can be used.

The simple relation between object distance, image distance, and focal length measured from the centre of the lens derived by geometrical optics for thin lenses gives

$$\frac{1}{u} + \frac{1}{v} = \frac{1}{f} \tag{3.17}$$

where u is the object distance, v the image distance, and f the focal length, and where all distances are measured from the principal plane of the lens using the 'real-is-positive' convention.

For a parallel beam corresponding to an object at infinity

$$\frac{1}{u} = \frac{1}{f} \tag{3.18}$$

The curvature for a material of refractive index n is given by

$$\frac{1}{f} = (n-1) \left(\frac{1}{R_1} - \frac{1}{R_2} \right) \tag{3.19}$$

where R_1 and R_2 are the radii of curvature.

The focal length for a thick lens is

$$f = \frac{-R_1 R_2}{(n-1)[R_1 - R_2 - (n-1)t/n]} \tag{3.20}$$

where t is the lens thickness, which if the thickness is small reduces to eq. 3.19.

The highest definition possible with a lens is limited by diffraction; however, the effect of other aberrations may be severe before this condition is reached and are often important in designing lens systems.

Variation of the angular diameter of the diffraction-limited image given by $\delta = 1.22\,F$ for various F numbers ($F = f/d$) where d is the aperture (beam width where the beam is smaller than the aperture), with wavelength is shown in Fig. 3.15.[34] The angular diameter δ is the angle ϕ subtended by the image at the focus at the centre of the lens, i.e., $\delta = \phi f$.

In practice the highest resolution of laser systems using spherical optics is normally limited by spherical aberration.

Spherical aberration can be minimized by special lens design or by the use of a correcting lens. Aberration is dependent on the curvature of the lens and decreases as the refractive index of the material increases, since the radius of curvature for a given focal length decreases with refractive index. The spherical aberration also decreases as the focal length of the lens is increased.

The angular diameter limited by spherical aberration is a minimum when

$$\frac{R_2}{R_1} = \frac{2n^2 + n}{2n^2 - n - 4} \tag{3.21}$$

At $n = 1.69$ the optimum value of R_2/R_1 changes from negative to positive, corresponding to a change from a convex lens to a meniscus convex-concave lens. The variation of the optimum ratio of radii of curvature is shown in Fig. 3.16 together with the optimum values for various common lens materials.

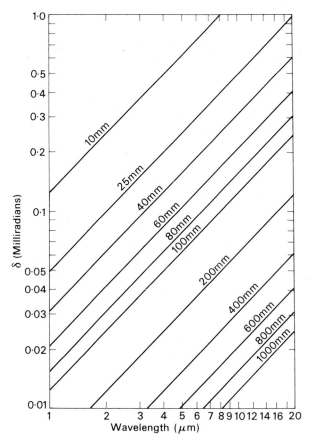

Fig. 3.15 *The angular diameter of the diffraction image of an optical system as determined by the aperture of the system and the wavelength of the radiation (after Scott, R. M., 'Optics for Infra-red Systems', Proc. IRE, 47 (9), 1530–1536, 1959)*

For the case of minimum spherical aberration we may write

$$f = -BR_1 \qquad (3.22)$$

which is shown in Fig. 3.16.

The approximations involved give rather smaller image sizes than found in practice, the error increasing at small F numbers, low index of refraction, or short radii of curvature. Typically for quartz at $F/1\cdot5$ the actual image will be 35 per cent greater and for germanium at $F/1$, 23 per cent larger, however, at double the F number the approximation is close in both cases.

The variation of the minimum angular diameter of images produced by lenses of typical materials with spherical surfaces chosen for minimum spherical aberration are shown in Fig. 3.17 as a function of the lens aperture. Comparison of the diffraction-limited angular diameter which is limited by the wavelength and aperture (Fig. 3.15) and the minimum angular diameter due to spherical aberration which is limited by the aperture and refractive index of the material (Fig. 3.17) indicates which is the principal factor limiting the resolution of a system.

Chromatic aberration results from the variation in angle of refraction at the interface of a material with the wavelength of the incident light due to dispersion. It can be reduced by combining lenses of different refractive indices. Chromatic aberration is often of little importance in considering laser systems since normally the output of the laser is monochromatic or very nearly so.

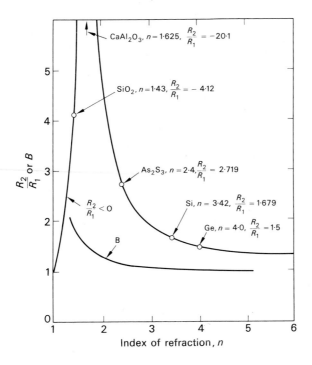

Fig. 3.16 *Ratio of radii of the surfaces of lenses for minimum spherical aberration and the value of the constant* B, *as they depend on the index of refraction (after Scott, R. M., 'Optics for Infra-red Systems',* Proc. IRE, **47** (9), *1530–1536, 1959)*

Coma is the lens defect that causes variation of magnification with aperture, of rays oblique to the lens. The name coma is derived from the comet-like appearance of the image. Aberrations due to coma are not encountered in laser systems where the incident ray is normal to the surface.

The performance of a lens may also be limited by its manufacturing tolerances. These include the surface finish which is normally to within $\lambda/20$ of the operating wavelength, the radius of curvature which governs the focal length, and the thickness and the alignment of the optical axis with the edge of the lens.

Methods used to mount lenses include the use of adhesives and optical cements and where the lens is required to be demountable, the lens assembly may screw into a fitting. Where water cooling is required the lens may be mounted between O-rings and the edge and face area adjacent to the edge cooled. Alternatively the lens may be mounted using an adhesive of good thermal conductivity in a heat sink which is cooled by natural or forced convection. Lens adjustment is obtained in a similar way to that described for laser mirrors.

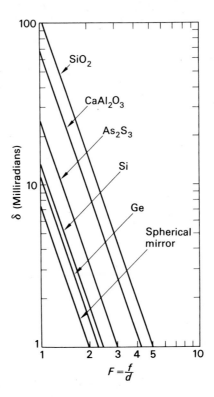

Fig. 3.17 *The angular diameter of images produced by lenses of typical materials with spherical surfaces chosen for minimum spherical aberration as dependent on the F number of the system (after Scott, R. M., 'Optics for Infra-red Systems', Proc. IRE, **47** (9), 1530–1536, 1959)*

3.4.1 Collimators Although the output of a laser has an inherently low divergence, this can often be further reduced with a collimator. Collimators are often used where the stable low order mode characteristics obtained by spherical laser optics result in excessive divergence of the laser beam or where expansion of the beam is required.

The divergence of a beam with a Gaussian intensity distribution is

$$\alpha = \frac{2}{\pi} \frac{\lambda}{r_o} \tag{3.25}$$

where α is half the angle of divergence, λ is the wavelength, and r_o the radius of beam at the output window.

The divergence of a projected beam may be reduced by first enlarging the beam, i.e., increasing r_o. If the beam is enlarged by the factor f_2/f_1 the divergence, which is inversely proportional to the beam diameter, decreases by the factor f_1/f_2.

Reflecting and refracting collimating systems are illustrated in Fig. 3.18. Various different reflection systems exist. Reflecting collimators are useful at wavelengths where transmission optics have appreciable losses, but are expensive and are used mainly in the infrared. The Cassegranian system is normally used.

Refracting collimators are mostly used over the visible and near visible region where relatively simple and cheap transmission optics are available.

56

Two lenses used in a Keplerian and Gallilean telescope configuration are shown in Fig. 3.18. The ratio of the beam diameters before and after the collimator is given by

$$\frac{d_2}{d_1} = \frac{f_2}{f_1} \tag{3.26}$$

It is possible to use a spatial filter or stop at the focus of the Keplerian configuration, but not in the case of the Gallilean telescope.

3.4.2 Special lenses Various special lens designs have been used for particular applications. Examples are cylindrical lenses which are capable of forming a line focus from a parallel beam and conical section (axicon) lenses.

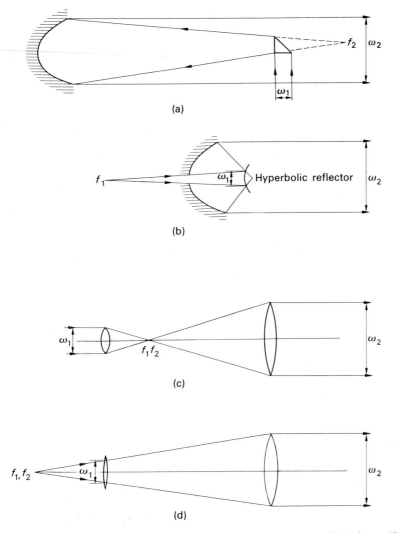

Fig. 3.18 *Reflecting and refracting collimators:* (a) *Newtonian;* (b) *Cassegranian;* (c) *Keplerian;* (d) *Gallilean*

The axicon lens[35] comprises a conical surface adjacent to the source; the second surface is normally flat. Parallel light is deflected through a fixed angle in a circularly symmetrical pattern. The lens focuses the parallel rays which are at an angle to the principal axis of the lens so that they are focused off-axis in a ring. Similar techniques may be used to produce a line or even a square at the focus.

3.5 Light guides

Fibre optics, in which flexible fibres of the transmitting material are used, enable a flexible light channel to be obtained. Transmission along the axis of the fibre is high due to total internal reflection at angles of incidence at the fibre walls greater than the critical angle. If the fibres retain the same relation to each other at the beginning and end, images may be transmitted and the fibre bundle is referred to as coherent. At present these techniques are limited to around the visible region and near infrared over which suitable low-loss transmitting materials are available.

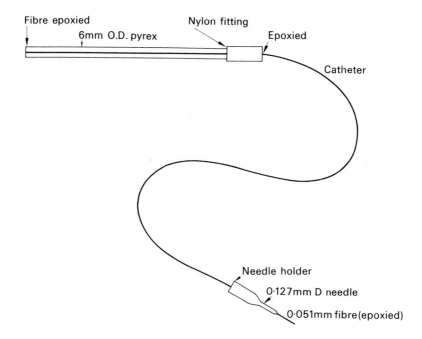

Fig. 3.19 *Schematic illustration of single-fibre laser probe (from Swope, C. H. and Innis, R. E., 'Fiber Optic Laser Devices', Ann. N.Y. Acad. Sci., **168** (3), 446–458, 1970)*

The fibre optic element itself can be doped with, for example, neodymium. The fibre can act as a laser and can be illuminated with a helical flash tube or by forming it in a helix surrounding a linear flash tube.[36] The laser output is transmitted along the length of fibre which is not pumped and which is transparent at $1·06\,\mu m$. A single fibre laser probe is shown in Fig. 3.19. Pulsed and CW power have been transmitted in this way. Potential application exists as a precision surgical instrument. (See also 4.3.2.)

3.6 Q switches

Q switches are extensively used in laser systems where output pulses of high peak power are required. Examples of Q switches are shown in Fig. 3.20. In the Q switched mode the laser is excited without feedback by preventing reflection from one of the end mirrors so that most of the laser levels are filled. The end mirror is suddenly allowed to reflect using a variety of methods including mechanical movement, electro-optic and acousto-optic devices or by a dye cell. The suddenly applied feedback from the mirror causes a rapid inversion of the excited level resulting in a high peak power output pulse with a rapid risetime.

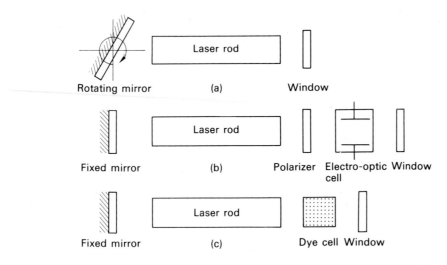

Fig. 3.20 *Mechanical and electro-optic Q switches*

Mechanically rotated multi-faced mirrors with externally reflecting surfaces are also used for Q switching. The time during which the mirror is 'on' is matched to the rise time of the laser pulse which is typically of the order of 10–30 ms for ruby. Switching times of about 1 μs are possible at very high rates over a wide range of wavelengths including the far infrared. Direct drive up to rotational speeds of around 36 000 rev/min may be used and can be effectively increased with multi-facet reflectors. Where very high speeds are required air drives are preferred due to the reduced vibration obtainable and speeds up to 200 000 rev/min are obtainable. Mechanically driven Q switches are suitable for use at a wide range of wavelengths with the appropriate mirror coating including 10·6 μm.[37] Mechanical Q switches generally have a lower insertion loss and enable a higher optical quality to be obtained than other Q switching techniques.

One form of passive Q switch uses a cell containing an organic dye that is reversibly bleached transparent by fluorescence from the laser. The cell is positioned between the laser rod and external mirror as shown in Fig. 3.20. Their use with ruby lasers has been extensively studied,[38,39] and they are also available for use at 1·06 μm.[40]

Initially the metastable laser states are filled. The light output from the laser rod builds up relatively slowly and is absorbed by the dye, preventing reflection from the mirror until the dye is bleached when a relatively high intensity has been reached.

Reflection from the mirror is possible and results in a rapid increase in cavity gain causing rapid depopulation and very high peak pulse powers may be achieved in this way.

For satisfactory operation the dye should have a peak absorption close to the output wavelength of the laser and be stable at the energies used. The desired optical density can be varied by altering the concentration of the dye. The cell itself has to be capable of transmitting the laser output and the faces through which the beam passes must be optically finished and are normally coated to reduce reflections. The life of the dye is normally several hundred laser pulses but may deteriorate due to exposure from ultraviolet or blue light. A solution of cryptocyanine in methanol is commonly used for ruby although various other solutions have been used.

The transmission of liquids and dyes is poor in the far infrared and gases have been used for passive Q switching at the output wavelength of the CO_2 laser using saturable absorbing gases instead of dyes.[41]

Although dye cells are normally cheap and simple and can be made to operate satisfactorily, their performance is often unpredictable and can vary over a period. The recovery rate is also relatively slow, limiting the maximum pulse repetition rate possible.

Various electro-optic bi-refringent materials have been used for Q switching using the Pockels effect. (See also 3.2.3.) ADP, KDP and K*DP, $LiNbO_3$, and α-HIO_3 have been used for Q switching ruby and neodymium lasers. Reduced delay between firing and transmission, repeatability, reliability, and ease of use are advantages over dye cells. The coherence length obtainable with a dye cell is, however, better than with a Pockels cell.

Mode-locking or phase-locking techniques force the modes to maintain equal frequency spacings and phase relationships to each other.[42] Mode locking can be used to generate very high peak power pulses of short duration using techniques similar to those used for Q switching with saturable dye cells. Brewster faces may be used at the ends of the laser and the dye cell to minimize unwanted reflections. The dye saturates corresponding to the spatial position of the peak intensity of the fluorescence in the laser cavity producing a narrow bleached region in the dye cell. Preferential stimulated emission of the corresponding mode then increases rapidly due to feedback from the front mirror resulting in the production of a very high power pulse of short duration.

Acousto-optic materials can also be used for Q switching. The transmission and acousto-optic properties of silica glasses are suitable for Q switching neodymium lasers at $1.06\,\mu m$. Repetitive switching rates of several kHz are obtainable enabling either high peak powers at low repetition rates or mean powers approaching the CW output at high switching rates ($> 1\,kHz$) to be achieved. Low insertion losses of less than 3 per cent in the on state but greater than 45 per cent in the off state are obtained. The on times lie between $0.5\,\mu s$ and $5\,\mu s$.

3.7 Wavelength selection

Wavelength selection can be carried out within the resonant cavity or externally. Various methods of wavelength selection are shown in Fig. 3.21. The advantage of intra-cavity wavelength selection is that relatively little power loss occurs since only the selected wavelength is amplified. The method of selection has itself to be efficient so that the gain of the cavity is not reduced below the feedback threshold for laser action to take place. Diffraction gratings, prisms, and tilted etalons can sometimes be used for intra-cavity wavelength selection where the cavity gain is adequate.

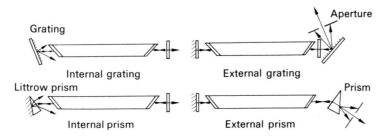

Fig. 3.21 *Methods of wavelength selection using reflection gratings and prisms*

External wavelength selection depends on the rejection of other wavelengths in the output beam and a corresponding loss in power. Gratings, prisms, and narrow band filters may be used.

One form of diffraction grating comprises a series of reflecting grooves with a triangular profile. The blaze angle is the angle which the reflecting surfaces make with the mean angle of the plane of the grating. The output wavelengths can be selected by rotating the grating about an axis parallel to the grooves. The wavelength is related to the angle of incidence at the grating such that

$$m\lambda = 2d \sin i$$

where m is an integer corresponding to the order of diffraction, d is the separation of the grooves, and i is the angle of incidence. From this the angle of the grating mount can be calibrated in terms of λ, the tuned wavelength.

Diffraction gratings may be used for the totally reflecting mirror of a laser enabling accurate stabilization at specific wavelengths to be achieved. The use of a grating for wavelength stabilization is illustrated in Fig. 3.21. The beam is first polarized in the plane of the grating lines. Only light at the grating is reflected perpendicularly along the laser axis and hence is amplified by the laser.

Intra-cavity wavelength selection can also be obtained by using the dispersion that can be achieved with a prism where the gain of the cavity is sufficient. The first face is mounted at the Brewster angle and the second has a reflecting coating. The prism is cut so that incident rays of the chosen wavelengths are deviated off-axis so that they are not amplified.

Single wavelength selection can also be obtained with a tilted etalon (see also section 3.3.1) which when tilted behaves as a frequency selective transmission filter. Frequencies close to its transmission peak are transmitted while other frequencies are rejected by reflection. A simple etalon placed in a laser cavity tilted at an angle θ has a maximum transmission at

$$m\theta = 2nt \cos \frac{\theta}{n} \tag{3.27}$$

where m is an integer (normally large) and t is the separation between the surfaces of the etalon. External wavelength selection is similar in action but the power associated with the unwanted wavelengths is wasted. Narrow band pass filters can also be used.

3.8 Spatial filters

A spatial filter comprises an aperture which may be very small, often with facilities for precisely aligning it. A pin-hole is an example of a spatial filter. Spatial filters may be inserted in the laser cavity to alter the mode structure or the beam shape.[43] Outside the laser they may be used to alter the beam shape only. In either case a loss in laser output power results although it is generally less for intra-cavity operation.

Spatial filters can be used to remove unwanted high order modes in the output of multimode lasers. A short focal length lens is used and the filter is placed in the plane of the focus. Depending on the aperture diameter, which is normally of the same value as the diffraction-limited beam size for the configuration, components of the incident beam other than those parallel to the optic axis of the filter and lens are focused outside the filter aperture. The beam may be re-collimated after the filter.

To minimize truncation circular apertures co-axial with a Gaussian beam should have a diameter greater than $1\cdot7\,\omega_0$ where ω_0 is the diameter at which the intensity is $1/e$ that at the centre, and preferably greater than $2\,\omega_0$ to reduce truncation to a negligible amount. Where the distribution is non-Gaussian the aperture should be similarly proportioned.

3.9 Optical attenuators

For many applications fixed or variable attenuation of the output of a laser is required. Around the visible region and at small power densities, neutral density filters can be used to attenuate the beam by absorption. Neutral density filters are normally specified by

$$T = 10^{-D/2}$$

where T is the transmission and D the optical density. At higher power densities attenuation by reflection of part of the output is preferable. Small attenuation ratios can be achieved by partial reflection in the same way as beam splitting. Increased attenuation can be achieved by a series of beam-splitting plates. Attenuation of polarized light can be varied over a wide range by rotating the beam splitter about the incident axis of the beam.

3.10 Detectors and calorimeters

Several methods exist for the measurement of the power and energy in laser beams.[44] Power measurement may be made indirectly by measuring the intensity of the beam or by direct calorimetry. Both methods have their limitations and in many practical cases the use of a calorimeter may not be so convenient but the results obtained are often more reliable.

The output power of a laser can be measured indirectly using devices relying on the photo-electric effect.[45] Examples are p-n junction diodes which may be used to generate a voltage or a resistance change with response time of less than 10^{-8} s. The spectral response of photodiodes is non-uniform and calibration is necessary for use at a specific wavelength. The use of photodiodes is typically limited to the range 0·3 μm to 1·1 μm. The accuracy obtainable depends on the calibration which may vary over long periods. The output is usually amplified and measured with a moving coil meter or digital indicator. If high powers are measured attenuation of the laser beam may be necessary.

Photomultipliers may be used to determine very low radiation levels but due to their highly non-linear spectral response and variation in sensitivity over the active surface, normally require calibration and are normally used only where a very high sensitivity is required. The range of wavelengths over which they are used depends on the internal phosphor coating and window material and varies from about 0·15 μm to 1·1 μm. Very rapid response times of the order of 10^{-9} s are possible.

The detection of power in the infrared region beyond about 1·5 μm presents special problems. Photo-electric detectors using the photo-voltaic or photo-conductive effect can be used, and various semiconductor detectors available for use in the infrared region beyond about 1 μm are shown in table 3.9.[46] Lead sulphide detectors have a

Table 3.9 *Semiconductor detectors for use in the infrared (after Stanley, C. R., 'Infra-red detectors for the range 1·5–30 μm', Optics and Laser Technology, 2 (3), 144–149, 1971)*

Detector	Normal Operating Temperature, K	Operating Range (μm)
PbS	273	visible to 3
InSb	273	visible to 7·5
$Hg_{1-x}Cd_xTe$	77	visible to 5·6
	273	1–5·5
AuGe	77	2–9
HgGe	4	2–13
CuGe	4	2–25

useful output up to 3 μm. Indium antimonide is sensitive from 2 μm to 13 μm and copper-doped germanium at 4·2 K from 2·25 μm. Cadmium telluride detectors are also suitable for use at wavelengths over the 3 μm–5·5 μm region; cryogenic cooling at 177 K with liquid nitrogen is normally required.

The characteristics of photodiodes, photomultipliers, and photoconductive detectors over the range 0·3 μm to 10·6 μm have been reviewed.[45]

Pyroelectric detectors capable of operation at room temperature without a window over a range of 0·5 μm to 1000 μm with a sensitive area of 1 mm^2 are also used in this region.[47,48] The absorbed radiation heats the detector altering the lattice spacing and results in a change in electric polarization below the Curie temperature. A change in current in an external circuit connected to electrodes on the crystal perpendicular to the axis of polarization occurs. Very rapid response times are possible, and thermal imaging systems using arrays of electrodes can be constructed.

Thermopiles comprising a large number of series-connected thermocouples can be used to measure the mean power output by measuring the temperature rise when placed in the laser beam. Thermopiles are suitable for the accurate indirect measurement of the total energy from pulsed lasers since the integrated output voltage is a measure of the total energy if the duration of the pulse is short so that adiabatic heating can be assumed. The output of a thermopile is independent of wavelength but variations in reflectivity may affect the accuracy of readings. Variations in heat loss will also cause errors and calibration against a known reference is desirable.

Calorimetric techniques may also be used to measure the output from high-power pulsed lasers and CW lasers.[49] Calorimeters relying on measurement of the total incident energy are normally most accurate and are used for absolute measurements. Reflection losses are minimized by using a conical inlet with a small angle of taper so that a large number of reflections occur before the beam leaves the cone and by the use of high absorption coatings where possible. The power output is measured from the rise in temperature of the calorimeter. A substandard calorimeter, Fig. 3.22, designed for measuring the output of pulsed lasers has been developed. The internal polished cone results in multiple reflections within the calorimeter.[50] A glass disc calorimeter has been developed for measuring high powers and pulse powers up to 50 J at power densities of 0·401 W/mm^2 have been measured.[51]

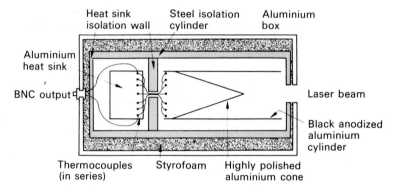

Fig. 3.22 *High energy pulsed laser power detector (from* NBS Technical News Bulletin, *55 (2), 45–46, 1971)*

For continuous measurement at high powers water-cooled calorimeters may be used and the difference in temperature of the cooling water at inlet and outlet measured with two thermocouples connected so that their outputs are in opposition (differential connection). This is usually small and the output may be increased by using several thermocouples connected in series and amplifying the output. A simple thermocouple calorimeter suitable for CO_2 lasers in which the temperature gradient is measured along a conducting path of known geometry has been described.[52]

Calorimeters have been made using bolometers in which the change in resistance of a conductor with increase in temperature is used as a measure of the incident power or energy. Like the thermopile the output is independent of wavelength except for variations in reflection losses. The heat loss can be compensated by separately heating the resistance electrically. When exposed to the beam of light the current is adjusted with a variable resistance in series with the bolometer until it is the same and hence the heat loss is identical. The variation in series resistance or the change in resistance of the bolometer can be used as a measure of the power of the incident beam. One form of bolometer uses a randomly wound length of wire appropriately referred to as a 'rat's nest calorimeter'. An alternative form uses a thin resistance film on a sapphire substrate one side of which is exposed to the laser output and the other water cooled. It is capable of operation between $0.4\,\mu m$ and $4.0\,\mu m$ at power densities up to $4\,W/mm^2$.

Other methods of determining the intensity distribution in high energy beams in the infrared region have been developed. An infrared sensitive scanning camera can be used to examine the output of a CO_2 laser giving a visual display in real time. The photon drag effect in germanium in which incident photons generate an e.m.f. which is proportional to the incident light has been used to determine power distribution and total output power in pulsed CO_2 laser beams and is capable of a very rapid response limited only by the transit time of light along the rod and the delay in the measuring circuit.[53] Since germanium transmits in the infrared, continuous monitoring of the beam is possible. A very small thermocouple traversed across a CO_2 laser beam, using a rotating disc with an aperture in it to reduce the heat input to an acceptable level, has also been used to measure the intensity distribution.[54]

Direct visual observation of the mode structure of lasers in the visible region is possible provided adequate protection from optical hazards is used. Photographs can be obtained by conventional methods in the visible and near infrared region.

Where direct observation is not possible, at high powers images of the mode structure have been obtained on foamed polystyrene,[55] infrared sensitive paper,[56] and hydrated salts.[57] An alternative and more sensitive method for CW lasers is the use of fluorescent screens, which are activated by exposure to ultraviolet light while simultaneously exposed to the laser beam. Local heating quenches the fluorescent states of the coating on the screen and results in a reduction in fluorescence so that regions of high intensity in the laser beam appear as dark zones on the fluorescent plate.[58] A similar method has been described which uses a phosphor whose fluorescence is enhanced as the temperature is increased.[59]

3.11 Scanning methods

Applications such as communications, data storage, computer memories, and display scan the laser beam over areas large compared with the beam diameter. Much of the work in this area has been of a proprietary nature and is in any case outside the scope of this book. Methods that have been used include mechanical, electro-optic, and acousto-optic techniques.[59, 60] The mechanical scanners using vibrating, torsion, or rotating reflecting surfaces are limited by inertia. Torsional scanning systems using a similar deflection system to the galvanometers used in light-sensitive recorders are capable of scanning rates of up to $20\,kHz$. Mechanically driven rotating systems using air motors to reduce vibrations are capable of operation up to around $200\,kHz$.

References

1. Billings, B. C. (Ed.) 'Optics', Section 6, *Am. Inst. Physics Handbook*, Ed. D. E. Gray, McGraw-Hill Inc., New York, 1972.
2. Holter, M. R., Nudelman, S., Suits, G. H., Wolfe, W. L., and Zissis, G. J., *Fundamentals of Infrared Technology*, Macmillan, New York, 1962.
3. Wolfe, W. L. and Ballard, S. S., 'Optical Materials Films and Filters for Infra-red Instrumentation', *Proc. IRE*, **47** (9), 1540–1545, 1959.
4. Kreidl, N. J. and Rood, J. L., 'Optical Materials', *Applied Optics and Optical Engineering*, chapter 5, Vol. 1, Ed. R. Kingslake, Academic Press, New York, 1965.
5. Catalogue, *Harshaw Optical Crystals*, Harshaw Chemical Co., Cleveland, Ohio.

6. Glass, A. J. and Guenther, A. H., 'Laser Induced Damage of Optical Elements' – A status report. *Appl. Opt.*, **12** (4), 637–649, 1973.

7. Harrigan, F., Klein, C., Rudko, R. and Wilson, D., 'Windows for High-Power Lasers', *Microwaves and Laser Technology*, **8** (1), 68–76, 1969.

8. Baumeister, P. and Pincus, G., 'Optical Interference Coatings', *Scientific American*, **223** (6), 59–75, 1970.

9. Holland, L., *Vacuum Deposition of Thin Films*, Chapman & Hall, London, 1956.

10. Costich, V. R., 'Multilayer Dielectric Coatings', *Handbook of Lasers*, pp. 155–170, Ed. R. J. Pressley, Chemical Rubber Co., Cleveland, 1971.

11. Hass, G. and Ritter, E., 'Optical Film Materials and their Applications', *J. Vacuum Science and Technology*, **4** (2), 71–9, 1967.

12. Cox, J. T., Hass, G. and Jacobus, G. F., 'Infra-red Filters of Anti-reflected Si, Ge, InAs and InSb', *J. Opt. Soc. Am.*, **51** (7), 714–718, 1961.

13. Eppers, W., 'Atmospheric Transmission', Section 3, *Handbook of Lasers*, pp. 39–154, Chemical Rubber Co., Ohio, 1971.

14. Catalogue Oriel Optics Corporation, 1972.

15. Torkington, P. and Thompson, H. W., 'Solvents for use in the Infra-Red', *Trans. Faraday Soc.*, **41**, 184–186, 1945.

16. Smith, W. J., *Modern Optical Engineering*, McGraw-Hill, New York, 1966.

17. Yariv, A., *Introduction to Optical Electronics*, Holt, Rinehart and Winston, New York, 1971.

18. Kaminow, I. P. and Turner, E. H., 'Linear Electrooptic Materials', *Handbook of Lasers*, pp. 447–459 (Ed. R. J. Pressley), Chemical Rubber Co., Ohio, 1971.

19. Harvey, A. F., *Coherent Light*, Wiley Interscience, London, 1970.

20. Hook, W. R. and Hilberg, R. P., 'Lossless KD*P Pockels Cell for High-Power Q Switching', *Appl. Opt.*, **10** (5), 1179–1180, 1971.

21. Bjorkholm, J. E., 'Relative Measurements of the Optical Non-linearities of KDP, ADP, LiNbO$_3$ and α-HiO$_3$', *IEEE J. Quantum Electron.*, **4** (11), 970–972, 1968 and correction, *IEEE J. Quantum Electron.*, **5** (5), 260, 1969.

22. Zverev, G. M., Levchuk, E. A. and Maldutis, E. K., 'Destruction of KDP, ADP and LiNbO$_3$ Crystals by Intense Laser Radiation', *Sov. Phys. JETP*, **30** (3), 400–403, 1970.

23. Singh, S., 'Non-Linear Optical Materials', *Handbook of Lasers*, pp. 489–525 (Ed. R. J. Pressley), Chemical Rubber Co., Ohio, 1971.

24. Nath, G., Mehmanesch, H. and Gsanger, M., 'Efficient Conversion of a Ruby Laser to 0·347μ in Low Loss Lithium Iodate', *Appl. Phys. Lett.*, **17** (7), 286–289, 1970.

25. Cheslez, R. B., Karr, M. A. and Geusic, J. E., 'Repetitively Q-Switched Nd:YAlG-LiO$_3$ 0·53μ Harmonic Source', *J. Appl. Phys.*, **41** (10), 4125–4127, 1970.

26. Harris, S. E., 'Tunable Parametric Oscillators', *Proc. IEEE*, **57** (12), 2096–2113, 1969.

27. Flinchbaugh, D. E., 'Accousto-Optic Techniques in Laser Communications', *Opt. Spectra*, **4** (8), 49–53, 1970.

28. Dixon, R. W., 'Photo-elastic Properties of Selected Materials and Their Relevance for Applications to Accoustic Light Modulators and Scanners', *J. Appl. Phys.*, **38** (13), 5149–5153, 1967.

29. Henderson, D. M. and Abrams, R. L., 'A Comparison of Acousto-optic and Electro-optic Modulators at 10·6μ', *Optics Communications*, **2** (5), 223–226, 1970.

30. Hass, G., 'Mirror Coatings', *Applied Optics and Optical Engineering*, pp. 309–330, Vol. 3, Ed. R. Kingslake, Academic Press, New York, 1965.

31. Dickson, L. D., 'Characteristics of a Propagating Laser Beam', *Appl. Opt.*, **9** (8), 1854–1861, 1970.

32. Falconer, I. S. and Peklo, E., 'A Simple Adjustable Holder for Laser Reflectors', *Rev. Sci. Inst.*, **42** (1), 1551, 1971.

33. Hopkins, R. E., 'Mirror and Prism Systems', *Applied Optics and Optical Engineering*, pp. 269–308, Vol. 3, Ed. R. Kingslake, Academic Press, New York, 1965.

34. Scott, R. M., 'Optics for Infra-Red Systems', *Proc. IRE*, **47** (9), 1530–1536, 1959.

35. Barber, R. B. and Linn, D. L., 'Some Novel Approaches in the Utilisation of Lasers in Material Processing', *Record of 10th Symposium on Electron, Ion and Laser Beam Technology*, pp. 225–230, Ed. L. Marton, *IEEE*, 1969; San Francisco Press.

36. Swope, C. H. and Innis, R. E., 'Fiber Optic Laser Devices', *Ann. NY Acad. Sci.*, **168** (3), 446–458, 1970.

37. Smith, D. C., 'Q Switched CO_2 Laser', *IEEE J. Quantum Electron*, **5** (6), 291–292, 1969.

38. Hercher, M., Chu, W. and Stockman, D. L., 'An Experimental Study of Saturable Absorbers for Ruby Lasers', *IEEE J. Quantum Electron*, **4** (11), 954–968, 1968.

39. Spaeth, M. L. and Sooy, W. R., 'Fluorescence and Bleaching of Organic Dyes for a Passive Q-Switch Laser', *J. Chem. Phys.*, **48** (5), 2315–2323, 1968.

40. 'Eastman Products for Laser Systems', Eastman Kodak Co., 1972.

41. Lee, S. M., Gamss, L. A. and Ronn, A. M., 'Passive Q switching of a CO_2-N_2-He Laser with Ethylene', *Chem. Phys. Lett.*, **7** (4), 463–464, 1970.

42. Smith, P. W., 'Mode-Locking of Lasers', *Proc. IEEE*, **58** (9), 1342–1357, 1970.

43. Boyer, G., Huriet, J. T. and Lamouroux, B., 'Micro-Machining by Beams of Coherent Light', *Optics and Laser Technology*, **2** (4), 196–199, 1970.

44. Zimmerer, R. W., 'Power and Energy Measurement', *Laser Focus*, **6** (9), 39–44, 1970.

45. Stanley, C. R., 'Infra-red Detectors for the Range 1·5–30 μm', *Optics and Laser Technology*, **3** (3), 144–149, 1971.

46. Melchior, A., Fisher, M. and Arams, F., 'Photodetectors for Optical Communication Systems', *Proc. IEEE*, **58** (10), 1466–1486, 1970.

47. Putley, E. H., 'Infra-red Application of the Pyroelectric Effect', *Optics and Laser Technology*, **3** (3), 150–156, 1971.

48. Doyle, W. M., 'Pyroelectric Detection: A New Tool for Infra-red Laser Applications', *Electro-Optics*, **1** (3), 7–9, 1971.

49. Scott, B. F., 'Laser Energy Measurement by Absolute Methods', 'Lasers and the Mechanical Engineer', *Proc. Instn Mech. Engrs*, **183** (3D), 56–64, 1968–69.

50. Neill, A. H., 'High Energy Light Detector for the Pulsed Ruby and Glass Lasers', *Appl. Opt.*, **9** (10), 2392–2393, 1970.

51. Edwards, J. G., 'A Glass Disc Calorimeter for Pulsed Lasers', *J. Phys. E.*, **3**, 452–454, 1970.

52. Offenberger, A. A., 'Analysis of a Thermocouple Laser Power Meter', *Appl. Opt.*, **9** (11), 2594–2956, 1970.

53. Gibson, A. F., Kimmit, M. F. and Walker, A. C., 'Photon Drag in Germanium', *Appl. Phys. Lett.*, **17** (2), 75–77, 1970.

54. Harry, J. E. and Lunau, F. W., 'Measurement of the Intensity Distribution in a CO_2 Laser Beam', *IEEE. J. Quantum Electron*, **7** (6), 276, 1971.

55. Meyerhofer, D., 'Measurement of the Beam Profile of a CO_2 Laser', *IEEE J. Quantum Electron*, **4** (11), 969–970, 1968.

56. Inaba, H., Kobayashi, T., Yamawaki, K. and Sugiyama, A., 'Direct Observation of Output Beam Patterns from N_2-CO_2 Laser at 10·6 μm by Thermal Development Method', *Infra-red Physics*, **7** (3), 145–149, 1967.

57. Condas, G. A., 'Use of Hydrated Salts as Visual CO_2 Laser Thermographic Screens', *IEEE J. Quantum Electron*, **4** (1), 40–41, 1968.

58. Bridges, T. J. and Burkhardt, E. G., 'Observation of the Output of a CO_2 Laser by a High Resolution Thermographic Screen', *IEEE J. Quantum Electron*, **3** (4), 168–169, 1967.

59. Condas, G. A., 'Phosphor System for Converting Far-Infrared Laser Radiation to Visible Light', *IEEE J. Quantum Electron*, **7** (5), 202–203, 1971.

60. Fowler, U. J. and Schlafer, J., 'A Survey of Laser Beam Deflection Techniques', *Proc. IEEE*, **54** (10), 1437–1444, 1966.

61. Holt, D., 'Laser Beam Deflection Techniques', *Opt. Technology*, **2** (1), 1–7, 1970.

4

INDUSTRIAL LASERS

The development of lasers has taken place very rapidly and is still continuing. Nevertheless, a general pattern of laser types, methods of excitation, and their characteristics have emerged. More recently, although new laser transitions are still being discovered, few are of industrial significance and there has been more emphasis on improvement of existing lasers resulting in increased output power, longer life, improved mode structure and reliability with emphasis on their suitability for use in specific industrial applications.

A very large number of materials have been shown to exhibit laser action under a variety of conditions. This chapter summarizes the important characteristics of lasers, particularly of those that are commercially available or show promise for future industrial applications, principally from an applications viewpoint. The various types of lasers are listed in table 4.1. A detailed treatment of the transition processes involved, the output wavelengths, and characteristics of individual laser types are given in the selected reading list at the end of the book.

Table 4.1 *Common laser types and methods of excitation*

Laser Type	Normal Operating Range (µm)	Normal Method of Excitation
Solid state	0·6–3	Optical
Gas (a) monatomic	0·2–3	Glow and arc discharge
(b) molecular	2–100	Glow discharge
(c) metal vapour	0·2–0·6	Glow discharge
Liquid organic dye	0·3–1·2	Flash tube and laser
Semiconductor	0·3–31	Electric field
Chemical	2–100	Chemical reaction

The principal characteristics of commercially available lasers are summarized in table 4.2. Some examples of commercially available lasers are shown in Fig. 4.1 (gas and dye lasers) and Fig. 4.2 (solid state and semi conductor lasers).

Table 4.2 *Principal characteristics of commercially available lasers*

Laser	Principal output wavelengths (μm)	CW output — Output power TEM$_{00}$	CW output — Output power Multimode	Pulse energy (J) TEM$_{00}$	Pulse energy (J) Multimode	Peak pulse power (W)	Pulse width (μs)	Beam diameter between $1/e^2$ points (mm)	Beam divergence (half angle) millirad	Efficiency per cent	Comments
Ruby	0·6943	0·025	—	1	4×10^2	10^8	3×10^{-3}–10^3	2–20	0·3–5	<0·1	High power pulsed output in visible region. Applications in holography, ophthalmology, fabrication
Nd^{3+} : YAG/glass	1·06	0·25–25	1–10^3	2×10^{-3}–3	1×10^{-3}–$6·5 \times 10^2$	10^9	1×10^{-2}–7×10^3	1–25	0·15–7·5	>1	High efficiency pulsed and CW outputs. Applications for range-finding and fabrication processes
Helium–neon	0·6328	6×10^{-5}–$7·5 \times 10^{-4}$	1×10^{-4}–$1·5 \times 10^{-1}$	—	—	—	—	0·73–10	0·125–3	<0·1	Low cost, visible output. Used for surveying, metrology, holography
	1·152	$0·3 \times 10^{-3}$–1×10^{-3}	—	—	—	—	—	0·8–1·5	0·5–0·75	<0·1	
	3·391	$1·5 \times 10^{-3}$	—	—	—	—	—	1·2–2	0·35–1·5	<0·1	
Helium cadmium	0·325–0·4416	2×10^{-2}–5×10^{-2}	5×10^{-2}	—	—	—	—	0·8–2·5	0·25–1	—	
Argon	0·3511–0·5145	1×10^{-3}–10	$1·5 \times 10^{-3}$–15	$2·5 \times 10^{-6}$–$2·6 \times 10^{-4}$	$1·5 \times 10^{-5}$–10^{-3}	—	2–10^2	0·65–4	0·25–1	<0·1	High power CW output tunable over visible and near UV. Uses include ophthalmology. holography
Krypton	0·3507–0·7993	2×10^{-3}–4	—	2×10^{-5}	6×10^{-5}	—	40	1–4	0·25–0·5	<0·1	High power CW output tunable over visible and near UV
Xenon	0·3645–0·5395	—	4×10^{-6}	—	9×10^{-5}–2×10^{-4}	—	0·3–1	2·4–4	1–2·75	<0·1	Pulsed output in visible region used for trimming thick and thin film circuits
Nitrogen	0·3371	—	—	—	3×10^{-6}–6×10^{-2}	—	3×10^{-3}–1×10^{-2}	2·5	0·38–1·5	—	High power pulsed output in near UV. Used for pumping some dye lasers
Carbon monoxide	5·2–5·7	—	—	—	10^{-3}–10^{-1}	—	0·1–0·25	5	1	—	
Carbon dioxide	9·2–10·8	—	3–10^4	4×10^{-3}–10^2	1–2×10^2	—	0·1–10^7	0·8–25	0·25–4	>10	High power output at high efficiency. Used for cutting and welding
Organic dyes	0·2650–0·9600	2×10^{-1}	—	—	2×10^3	2×10^8	—	2–5	0·2–3	<0·1	Output tunable over broad range. Applications in spectroscopy, pollution detection, etc.
Gallium arsenide	0·85–0·905	—	1	—	5×10^{-6}	24†	0·1–1	$0·2 . 10^{-3} \times 40 . 10^{-3}$‡	200	1–40	Small size but high divergence. Uses include range-finding and pollution detection

* Normal operating mode.
† At room temperature.
‡ Dimensions of emitting region.

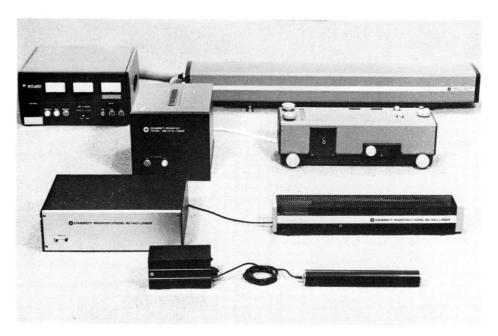

Fig. 4.1 (a) *Ion laser 0·5 W–4 W CW (0·351 μm–0·8 μm).* (b) *Tunable CW dye laser with external laser pump source (0·42 μm–0·7 μm).* (c) *Helium cadmium laser 10 mW CW (0·4416 μm).* (d) *Helium neon laser 2 mW (0·6328 μm).* (*Courtesy Coherent Radiation Ltd*)

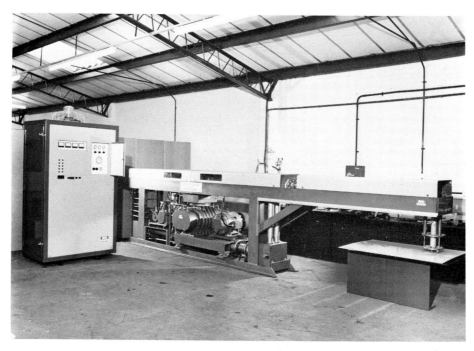

(e) CO_2 *laser 2 kW (10·6 μm) (laser cavity is in centre, cantilevered section includes beam traverse).* (*Courtesy BOC Industrial Laser Systems Ltd*)

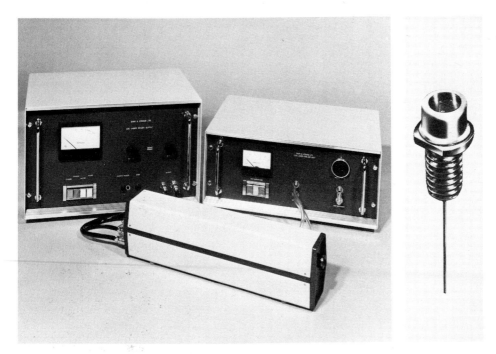

Fig. 4.2 (a) *Solid state ruby laser (0·638 μm) Q switched 10^7 W peak power at 25 ppm, pulse length 20 μs. (Courtesy Barr and Stroud Ltd)* (b) *GaAs diode laser. Wavelength of peak radiant intensity 0·954 μm maximum output power 24 W at 1000 pps with pulse duration of 14 μs. (Courtesy RCA Corporation)*

4.1. Solid-state lasers

Solid-state lasers consist of a host material in which the laser material is dispersed and are excited by optical radiation. The host material must not be detrimental to the laser process, should be transparent to the exciting radiation, and must possess good thermal and optical properties. A large number of crystalline materials have been used.[1]

The most efficient and generally preferred pumping method is to use the elliptical configuration shown in Fig. 4.3 with the linear pumping source along one principal axis (focus) and the laser rod on the other.[2] The coupling is dependent on the ratio of the radii of the source and the laser rod, the eccentricity of the ellipse, the length of the semi-major axis, and the angular distribution of the source radiation. For efficient coupling of the output of the pumping source to the laser rod both should be of approximately the same diameter and length. Double or multi-lobe reflectors with a pumping source at one focus of each ellipse and the laser rod at the common focus are sometimes used to increase the total power output although the coupling efficiency is lower than that of a single ellipse.[3]

The inside surface of the ellipse is made highly reflecting. Depending on the absorption bands of the laser material diffuse or specular coatings of gold, silver, or aluminium are used. Dielectric coatings with a high reflectivity over a narrow band of wavelengths are also used. The discharge tubes are normally straight or π-shaped and may be cooled by natural or forced convection or by water cooling.

Helically wound flash tubes are also used with the laser rod mounted on the axis

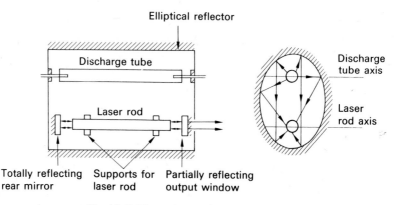

Fig. 4.3 *Solid state laser with elliptical reflector*

of the helix with a tubular external reflector. A higher pumping power than that obtainable with linear tubes is possible since the length of the flash tube is not limited by the length of the laser rod.

Laser operation can be obtained by coating the ends of the laser rod to form totally and partially reflecting mirrors. However, thermal distortion due to high and continuous or rapidly pulsed outputs can cause instability, excessive divergence, degradation of the mode structure, and damage to the coating itself. The alternative method is to position the laser rod accurately with respect to external mirrors which can be aligned with precision. This requires a very rigid common structure, normally a heavy channel section of an alloy with a low coefficient of expansion. A further advantage of external mirrors is the ability to use intra-cavity components such as Q switches or modulators. The end faces of the crystal may be cut at the Brewster angle as shown in Fig. 4.4 to plane polarize the light output and eliminate reflection losses in the plane of polarization. Where external mirrors are required at moderate power levels anti-reflection coatings may be used on the ends of the laser rod. Internal feedback due to internal reflection at high powers can be reduced by slightly misaligning the end faces in the plane transverse to the plane of the Brewster angle. By cutting the end faces anti-parallel feedback from internal reflection is reduced and the external mirror and window are on the same axis, simplifying the mechanical construction but resulting in a difference in path length which may be undesirable in some applications.

The peak pulse power output of solid-state lasers is generally proportional to the volume of the crystal. The continuous or mean pulsed power output is governed largely by the rate of dissipation of thermal energy in the crystal and is a function of the thermal properties of the material, the length, and the surface area. A combination of the poor thermal conductivity of available host materials, the absorption and attenuation of pumping radiation, and development of whispering modes tends to limit the diameter of the laser rod to about 10 mm for continuous or high repetition rate lasers.

Pumping across the end face of the laser is also possible and enables more uniform radiation to be obtained over a large effective area so that a high energy output is achieved without some of the non-uniformities that occur with cylindrical lasers. The laser normally takes the form of a disc whose length is small compared with its diameter. A variety of other pumping configurations have been used for special applications.

The laser output and mode structure is affected by thermal gradients in the laser rod resulting in curvature of the end faces and radial variation in refractive index. At a low value of power these effects may also cause saturation (above which increase in pumping energy does not result in a proportional increase in output power) due to poor utilization of the volume of laser material.

The divergence of solid-state lasers varies inversely with the length and is greatest for small diameter rods. The divergence of CW lasers is higher than that for pulsed lasers due to the greater effect of thermal expansion distorting the cavity. The divergence of solid-state laser rods with end coated mirrors is normally higher than that for separate end mirrors due to the distortion of the mirrors and reduced mirror separation.

4.2 Pumping sources for solid-state lasers

Optical pumping sources for solid-state lasers include flash lamps, continuous discharge tubes, incandescent lamps, and solid-state light sources. Optical sources for pumping lasers have been reviewed[4] and data on lamps that are commercially available summarized.[5] Some of the factors that govern the choice of lamp, its operating conditions, and lamp life are discussed below.

4.2.1 Flash lamps
Flash lamps are used to optically excite pulsed lasers, and operate in the regions E–G of the discharge characteristic in Fig. 4.5.

This region is typical of arc discharges but for pulses of short duration the equilibrium condition shown by the discharge characteristic may never be reached (i.e., the discharge voltage is greater for a given current). The output obtainable varies from single very high energy output pulses of short duration to a series of pulses of lower energy over a long period.

Flash lamps for high energy output pulses have a high mechanical strength necessary to resist the shock wave generated by the discharge and thermal shock. Thermal dissipation is not normally important if their use is intermittent but for repetitive operation, water cooling or forced convection may be used. Cooling, however, results in condensation of electrode materials and particles of silicon and silicon oxides evaporated from the quartz tube. For repetitive operation a higher filling pressure of several atmospheres is necessary. The lower specific working load (SWL) (the number of Joules dissipated in the discharge per unit volume of the discharge tube) necessary for repetitive flashes results in a longer life. The higher pressure also reduces the evaporation of electrode material and reduces the breakdown voltage that occurs

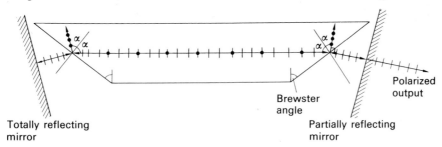

Fig. 4.4 *Solid state laser with Brewster-cut end faces*

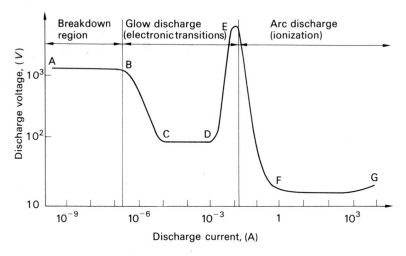

Fig. 4.5 Voltage–current discharge characteristic

with repetitive operation that results in a decrease in a dissipated energy. The electrodes may also outgas resulting in contamination of the gas and devitrification may occur resulting in the walls of the tube becoming opaque.

Common discharge tube configurations are linear, π, and helical and are illustrated in Fig. 4.6. Linear tubes used singly or in multiple configuration in a suitable reflecting system are normally most efficient, can be focused easily, and are widely used for commercial lasers. Helical flash tubes give the most uniform illumination and allow the highest power levels to be obtained without damage due to the development of hot

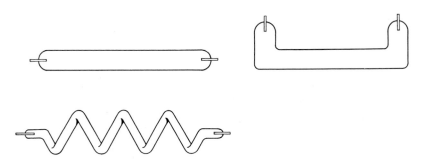

Fig. 4.6 Linear, π, and helical discharge tubes

spots. This is important in high-energy systems such as those used in mode-locked operation and for frequency doubling and quadrupling where the overall efficiency is low. Electrode separations in the flash tube are normally chosen to equal the length of the laser rod and can be 150 mm or more. The percentage of total input power lost at the electrodes and electrode effects decreases as the electrode spacing and hence discharge voltage is increased. The electrode spacing, gas, and gas pressure affect the impedance of the discharge which usually lies between $0 \cdot 1\,\Omega$ and $10\,\Omega$. The internal diameter of flash tubes varies between 2 mm and 30 mm. Where linear or π-shaped tubes are used the tube diameter should be approximately equal to the diameter of the laser rod.

Ideally the spectrum of the output of the discharge, which is governed primarily by the gas and gas pressure, should be matched to the absorption bands used to pump the laser material. Spectral data for argon, krypton-xenon, and neon filled flash lamps have been measured.[6] In practice the tubes are normally filled with xenon for which the highest total light output is obtained partly due to its low ionization potential. The design and characteristics of xenon-filled flash tubes have been described.[7] Flash tubes filled with krypton, neon, and xenon with oxygen are also available for special applications. The tube walls are normally made of quartz although borosilicate glass can be used with some sacrifice in light output and mechanical properties.

The efficiency of conversion of input energy at the electrodes to radiated output (excluding losses in the tube walls) ranges from about 20 per cent of the input energy at the electrodes of the flash tube to 50 per cent for large electrode separations and quartz tubes. The pressure in the tube depends on the repetition frequency and for single pulse discontinuous operation is of the order of 600 torr. The effect of increasing the pressure is to increase the light output particularly at short wavelengths and reduce sputtering effects at the electrodes but decreases the life of the lamp. As the pressure is increased further (depending on tube diameter) the light output tends to decrease due to self absorption, and increased mechanical strength is necessary.

The maximum output of a lamp is based on its specific working load (SWL). This is determined by the requirements of a high output and useful life and should be below 70 per cent of the energy at which the flash tube explodes; above this value the lamp life rapidly decreases. Typical values for the SWL are $0.1 \, J/mm^3$–$0.15 \, J/mm^3$ for a flash duration of about 1 ms.

Table 4.3 *Typical lifetimes of representative flash tubes*

Discharge Tube Type	Energy (J)	Discharge Length (mm)	Number of Flashes
Helical	10^4	75	10^4
Helical	60	75	8×10^6
Linear	100	37	10^3
Linear	200	75	$5 \times 10^3 - 10^5$
Linear	600	100	2×10^4
Linear	1.7×10^3	100	10^3
Linear	7.7×10^3	100	50

The life of the lamp may be measured in terms of the number of pulses or duration of continuous operation until catastrophic failure (normally by shattering of the tube walls) occurs. Alternatively, the life can be measured in terms of the time taken for the light output to decrease to a fraction (normally half) of its original value.

The life of the flash tube is a function of arc length, power, and repetition rate. The effect of increasing the output power above the rated value is to shorten the life substantially. Typical lifetimes of flash tubes are summarized in table 4.3 for helical flash tubes with an illuminated length of 75 mm. Typical lifetimes of linear tubes are 10^3 flashes at 100 J and a discharge length of 37 mm, 5×10^3 to 10^5 at 75 mm at 200 J, and

10^5 at 1700 J and 100 mm length. With very high peak pulses of short duration so that damping beyond the critical value is not possible, as in Q-switched systems, the flash tube life may be very much shorter.

Various methods may be used to trigger flash tubes. A discharge will normally occur across a gap between two electrodes at a voltage governed by the electrode separation and operating pressure and electrode geometry, temperature, etc., and will tend to vary during the lamp life from pulse to pulse.

The use of a separate high-voltage low-current triggering supply to initiate the discharge enables more precise control of the discharge to be achieved. Typical trigger voltages of around 10 kV are used although requirements of different tubes vary between 200 V and 30 kV. The triggering voltage provides an ionized path in the tube assisting the breakdown of the electrode gap by the main power supply. The trigger supply may be connected in series or parallel with the supply. The oscillatory frequency of the trigger source is normally high so that it can be easily filtered in the power supply circuit. Connection may be made directly to the electrode circuit or in some cases a separate trigger electrode or even a wire wrapped round the flash tube may be used. Unfortunately the use of a trigger pulse contributes to increased electrode losses.

Where very high power discharges are required 'over volted' discharges may be used with series spark gaps. The supply voltage is greater than the breakdown voltage of the tube so that when the spark gap is triggered breakdown of the main gap occurs. Even where the flash tube is precisely triggered at a known and repeatable voltage, the light output from the flash tube can vary from pulse to pulse by significant amounts due to changes in the discharge conditions.

4.2.2 Lamps for continuous lasers Continuous discharge lamps operate over the region FG of the discharge characteristic in Fig. 4.5 characterized by an arc discharge in thermal equilibrium.

Arc lamps are capable of continuous operation but at lower mean power outputs than flash lamps. The electrode gap is of the same order as the length of the laser rod, around 100 mm. The lamps are normally filled with high pressure xenon, krypton, or mercury vapour. Linear tubes are normally used but co-axial configurations have been used. As high an efficiency as possible is required since the life of the lamp at high power is limited by the power dissipated. Water cooling is normally necessary and also reduces the thermal energy dissipated in the lamp and radiated to the laser rod.

The output of krypton-filled discharge lamps has a radiated efficiency over the range 0·3 μm–1·2 μm of 61 per cent and an intense line output at 0·81 μm which is efficiently absorbed by neodymium doped laser hosts. A lamp life of 60 h at 15 kW input with an arc length of 200 mm at a gas pressure of 2 bar has been obtained. High pressure mercury arc lamps have also been used to obtain stimulated emission from ruby and neodymium–calcium tungstate, and the efficiency is typically 15 per cent to 40 per cent.

The lamp life of continuous discharge lamps is normally governed by devitrification of the discharge tube walls, evaporation of material onto the walls and fracture of the tube. During the life of the tube the light output for a given power output decreases progressively. The lamp life which may be a thousand hours for a krypton lamp operating at 30 W decreasing to a few hundred hours at powers over a hundred watts decreases very rapidly as the power is increased above 1 kW.

High-power tungsten–iodine lamps of about 1 kW have been used to pump low-power neodymium lasers with CW power outputs up to about 10 W (using two lamps). Although the total power output obtainable is small and the efficiency lower than that of a discharge lamp the peak in intensity is about 0·8 μm, close to the absorption line of neodymium and the overall effectiveness is comparable at low power with the xenon-filled discharge tubes. For low-power applications tungsten–iodine incandescent lamps have the advantage of simplicity, long life, and low cost.

Semiconductor lamps have also been used to pump low-power YAG-lasers with low threshold values. The relatively high conversion efficiency and the ability to select the wavelength at which the peak intensity occurs enables a high coupling efficiency between the absorption characteristic of the laser and the peak output of the lamp to be obtained.

4.2.3 Power supplies for optically pumped lasers Optically pumped lasers normally operate in the pulsed mode and use pulsed power sources to supply the flash tubes.

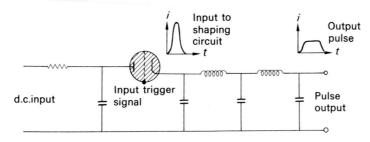

Fig. 4.7 *Pulsed power source and pulse shaping circuit*

Pulsed power supplies use capacitors to store the energy supplied from a d.c. source. A typical power supply with pulse-shaping circuit is shown in Fig. 4.7. Repetitively pulsed and CW power supplies use constant current rather than constant voltage discharge circuits. The stored energy in the capacitors is given by

$$J = \tfrac{1}{2}CV^2 \tag{4.1}$$

where J is the stored energy and C is the capacitance.

The pulse energy is normally varied by varying the supply voltage. The duration and shape of the pulse may be controlled to some extent by the pulse-shaping circuit. To prevent oscillation of the output sufficient resistance is incorporated to critically damp the output (i.e., when the circuit resistance $R > \sqrt{(4LC)}$). Where very high peak power and rapid rise times are required the inductance is reduced to a minimum and damping may be reduced below the value required for critical damping.

4.3 Solid-state laser materials

A large number of solid-state materials have been shown to exhibit laser action over a wide range of different wavelengths. Of these a small number enable an efficient population inversion to be obtained at room temperature. Up to now only ruby and the neodymium-doped laser hosts have been developed commercially.

4.3.1 Ruby Ruby was the first material shown to exhibit laser action in 1960 and has been extensively studied.

Ruby is a crystalline form of aluminium oxide (sapphire), doped with chromic oxide, Cr_2O_3, at about 0·3 per cent concentration, and is obtainable in large rods and discs. The characteristic wavelength of the laser emission is 0·6943 μm in the visible region of the spectrum with a divergence of about 1 to 5 milliradians. The output is normally pulsed and the laser is excited by pulsed discharge tubes filled with xenon. Coated end faces and external dielectric coated mirrors are used depending on the power and application. Repetitive pulsed, and CW operation[9] have also been achieved but are limited by overheating of the ruby due to the large pumping powers required and narrow absorption bands of ruby.

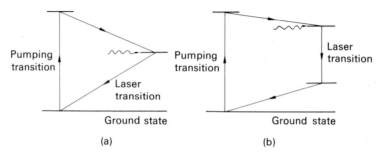

Fig. 4.8 *Three- and four-level laser transitions*

Ruby has a three-level laser transition. The transition levels are illustrated in Fig. 4.8(a) in a simplified form. For laser action to occur, the population of the ground state has to be inverted to the laser transition level. This is an inefficient process in the case of ruby and high pumping powers of the order of tens of joules are required and conversion efficiencies of only about 0·05 per cent are normally achieved.

The main areas of use for ruby lasers are where high pulse power outputs (up to about 10^{12} W) are required or where the visible output is useful, such as in holography. A coherence length in excess of 1 m is obtained using a dye cell to Q switch the output. Q switching and oscillator–amplifier configurations using the output from one ruby to pump a second are possible and very high pulse powers may be obtained in this way.

Ruby lasers are apparently reaching their limit of development. For fabrication processes involving melting or vaporizing materials that require large repetitive pulses of power they are being superseded by neodymium lasers which are considerably more efficient. Ruby lasers are likely, however, to continue to find applications where a high pulse power in the visible range of the spectrum is required.

4.3.2 Neodymium Neodymium-doped laser materials have a characteristic output wavelength of 1·06 μm. Pulsed and CW outputs are obtainable. The host materials that are used include yttrium aluminium garnet (YAG), yttrium orthoaluminate $YAlO_3$ (YALO), yttrium iron garnet YFe_5O_{12} (YIG), glasses, and calcium tungstate ($CaWO_4$) and have been extensively reviewed.[10] Neodymium in YAG has been most extensively studied.[11]

Neodymium has a four-level transition, Fig. 4.8(b). The laser transition is more easily inverted with respect to the intermediate transition level than the three-level transition of ruby. Pumping of the laser rod is normally by pulsed or continuous discharge tube and pumping at low levels of CW power output by incandescent lamps is also possible. Threshold pumping levels of 2 J–3 J at 2–3 per cent conversion efficiency can be obtained which in many cases outweighs the disadvantage of the output being in the invisible infrared. Frequency doubling is often used to give a visible output at $0.53\,\mu m$ at higher efficiencies than ruby.

The relative performance of various flash and continuous discharge lamps and CW tungsten–iodine lamps for pumping YAG lasers is shown in Fig. 4.9. For pulsed operation flash lamps filled with krypton are more efficient,[12] but at high current densities where the highest output is required xenon is more efficient.[13] Xenon-filled flash lamps are more efficient for pumping glass rods due to the higher absorption at $0.59\,\mu m$ where xenon has a higher output.[12] At moderate levels of pulsed power and at continuous outputs krypton-filled high-pressure discharge tubes are more efficient due to the high peak intensity of the output of krypton at $0.810\,\mu m$ close to the absorption line of neodymium. At high peak current densities and at pulse outputs around 10–40 J input depending on the pressure and current density, the resonance radiation corresponding to specific wavelengths decreases relative to the continuum radiation and the xenon-filled flash tube becomes more efficient.

For low-power continuous operation (10 W) tungsten–halide incandescent lamps[14] and mercury arc lamps with alkali additives may be used.[15] More recently, solid-state GaAs–P light sources whose output in the near infrared is close to the absorption line of Nd at $0.81\,\mu m$, have been used in experimental arrays to obtain laser action from YAG.

Each host material has advantages for certain applications, largely depending on the thermal properties of the host. YAG crystals have been most widely used up to now and are suitable for single and high repetition pulse rates and CW output. At high powers ultraviolet light from the pumping source results in the creation of colour centres (solarization). This can be minimized by using a separate glass filter to cut off the short wavelengths or by coating the rod with a suitable absorbing material. Continuous output of over 1000 W has been obtained from a single YAG crystal at efficiencies up to about 4 per cent with a divergence of about 3 milliradians.[16]

Neodymium-doped glass has been extensively studied.[17] Neodymium-glass laser rods are capable of higher peak pulse output than either YAG or calcium tungstate and can be readily obtained in large rods or discs. Glass is not suitable for high repetition rates or high power continuous operation due to variation in refractive index of the glass with temperature. Solarization also occurs at high powers. Pulse energies of 300 J in $3 \cdot 10^{-9}$ s, corresponding to peak pulse powers of 10^{11} W have been obtained.

Neodymium-doped glass can be used to produce low-power CW and pulsed flexible fibre-optic lasers.[18] Pulse powers of 100 kW at 5000 pulses a second have been achieved. Efficient coupling can be obtained by coiling the fibre around the pumping source in a helix. (See also Section 3.5.)

Calcium tungstate crystals are about a third of the cost of YAG crystals and are claimed to be more efficient over a narrow range of operation around 10 pulses a second. Calcium tungstate is not as efficient for high-power continuous operation and the peak pulse power output is less than that of neodymium glass.

At high CW powers, forced convection or water cooling by contact with the laser rod may be used. Thermal limitations on laser output and mode structure can be

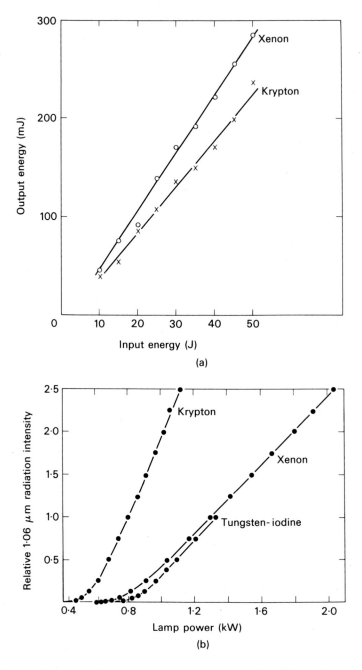

Fig. 4.9 *Relative performance of flash and CW lamps for pumping YAG : Nd³⁺ lasers.* (a) *Output energy of a Nd³⁺ doped YAG laser as a function of input energy for both xenon and krypton flash tubes (from Davies, M. B., Sharman, P. and Wright, J. K., 'Comparison of the Performance of Krypton and Xenon Filled Flash Tubes for Pumping Nd³⁺ Doped YAG Lasers', IEEE J. Quantum Electron.,* **4** *(6), 424–425, 1968).* (b) *Relative performance of krypton, xenon, and tungsten–iodine lamps for the continuous pumping of YAG : Nd³⁺ (from Read, T. B., 'The CW Pumping of YAG : Nd³⁺ by Water Cooled Krypton Arcs', Appl. Phys. Lett.,* **9** *(9), 342–344, 1966)*

reduced by suitable design of the laser rod using segmented rod construction to improve the effectiveness of the cooling, and sleeving with a material transparent to the pumping radiation minimizes effects due to non-uniform cooling.[19] Alternative methods of construction enabling very high output powers to be achieved have used large single crystals of high quality illuminated over the end face. Multiple series crystal discs arranged in the zig-zag configuration shown in Fig. 4.10 are used enabling efficient pumping by exposing large surface areas to the pumping radiation and more effective cooling of large volumes of laser material to be achieved.

The neodymium group of lasers is likely to find progressively wider application in industrial fabrication processes as output powers, particularly using YAG crystals, are increased.

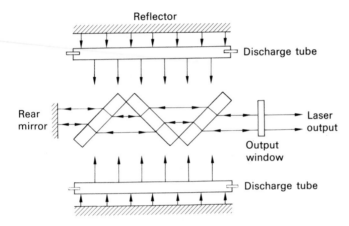

Fig. 4.10 *Face-pumped zig-zag disc laser configuration*

4.4 Gas lasers

A large number of gases have been shown to exhibit laser action.[1] Of these, rather more have become available commercially than solid-state laser materials, due to the greater variation in output parameters. The principal gas lasers available are the helium–neon, argon ion, and CO_2 lasers, all of which have been extensively studied[20, 21] and widely used for industrial application. Various other gas lasers are available from a limited number of sources but have not been widely used in industry.

A typical gas laser cavity is shown in Fig. 4.11. The pumping source is normally an

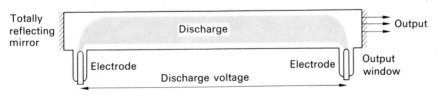

Fig. 4.11 *Gas laser with axial discharge*

electrical discharge which may be directly coupled (d.c., power frequency, or r.f.) or indirectly coupled without electrodes (r.f.). The discharge is along the axis of the laser between pairs of recessed electrodes. Hot (thermonic) and cold cathodes can be used, but cold cathodes which do not require a separate heater supply and are more robust than thermonic cathodes are usually preferred.

Uniform excitation of a larger volume of gas enabling higher powers to be obtained is possible with a discharge transverse to the optic axis of the laser. Transverse discharges (Fig. 4.12) can be used to excite electron and molecular lasers. A stable continuous discharge is not possible and single pulse and repetitive discharges are used.

Excitation is also possible by electron beams, chemical transitions, and transitions induced by sudden changes in pressure by expansion through a nozzle.

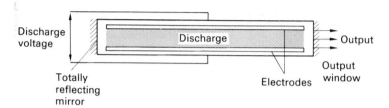

Fig. 4.12 *Gas laser with transverse discharge*

The end windows can be mounted at the Brewster angle at either end of the tube so that external mirrors may be used and intracavity modulation can also be carried out. The output is, however, plane polarized which in some cases is a disadvantage. The cavity walls of atomic and molecular lasers are normally borosilicate glass which at high powers may be water cooled. Refractory materials are used for the walls of ion lasers.

4.4.1 Power supplies for gas lasers Most gas lasers are excited by an electric discharge inside the laser cavity. Electrical discharges are influenced by a variety of external parameters but are largely dependent on the gas, gas pressure, and current. The discharge characteristic is similar to that of discharge tubes shown in Fig. 4.5.

Electronic transitions such as those of the helium laser are excited in the glow discharge region C–D in Fig. 4.5 at about 10 mA and gas pressures of about 2 torr. The axial flow CO_2 laser which depends on molecular vibrational transitions operates over the region B–C at a current of about 50 mA and at a pressure of 10 torr. The argon laser, which depends on ionization occurring for excitation to take place, operates over the region F–G at currents of several amps with an operating voltage of about 150 V at a pressure of 0·25 torr.

Operation of CW gas lasers is normally from rectified a.c. At low powers rectified single-phase a.c. is used but at high powers three-phase rectification may be used. Radio-frequency power supplies enable electrode-less operation by inductive excitation of the gas but are expensive and seldom used. Pulsed lasers use similar power supplies to flash tubes (see section 4.2.3). High-frequency repetitively pulsed discharges are also used for some types of transverse discharge lasers.

The maximum supply voltage should be sufficient to cause initial breakdown between the electrodes in the laser cavity. For stable operation the voltage across the discharge is usually about half the open-circuit voltage. Alternatively, a separate high-voltage surge injection source may be used to initiate the discharge.

Modulation of the power output of gas lasers can be achieved by varying the output of the power supply although the laser response may not be linear. Saturable reactors on the input side of the power transformer, or thyristor control either on the input of or in place of the rectifiers enable modulation at low frequencies. Valves and high-power transistors can be used for modulation at higher frequencies.

4.5 The principal gas lasers

Three principal gas laser transition mechanisms exist:

(a) Electronic transitions in neutral atoms
(b) Electronic transitions in ions
(c) Vibrational transitions in molecular gases

The method of operation and construction of lasers using these processes is often similar.

4.5.1 The helium–neon laser
The helium–neon laser is typical of the neutral atom type of laser in which laser action results from electron transitions and has been studied in detail.[22] Although the output wavelength of helium–neon lasers most often used is at 0·6328 μm a wide range of output wavelengths can be obtained including useful outputs in the near infrared. Some of these are shown in table 4.4 with the approximate levels of output power obtainable corresponding to a maximum output at 0·6328 μm of 25 mW.

Table 4.4 *Some of the more important output wavelengths obtainable from helium–neon lasers*

Output Wavelength (μm)	Power (mW) (Single mode)
0·6118	2
0·6328	25
1·084	10
1·152	12
3·381	5

The helium–neon laser is normally excited by a continuous axial discharge with a heated coated cathode or cold aluminium or zirconium cathode although pulsed discharges, r.f. induction coupled, and transverse discharges have also been used.

External reflectors with the tube windows at the Brewster angle are often used.

Continuous operation at up to several hundred milliwatts at an overall efficiency of about 0·003 per cent at 0·6328 μm can be obtained. The divergence (half angle) can be made less than 1 mrad in single-mode operation and peak pulse outputs of up to 1 W are possible. Single-mode operation is easily achieved and high spectral purity and a coherence length in excess of 1 m are obtainable.

Precise stabilization of the wavelength of the output of the helium–neon laser can be obtained from the Lamb dip effect,[22] which corresponds to a wavelength at which the intensity passes through a minimum. The effect can be readily observed with single-mode helium–neon lasers but is not peculiar to them. The wavelength at which the intensity is a minimum can be accurately and repeatedly selected by varying the cavity length using a piezo-electric translator on the end mirror, and is used for precision wavelength measurements. The stability of the output of a helium–neon laser at $3 \cdot 39 \, \mu m$ has been measured as 1 part in 10^8 by comparison with krypton standards, limited only by the accuracy of the krypton standard.

The helium-neon laser has reached an advanced stage of development. Co-axial designs suitable for mass production have been developed. It is already available in portable forms for use on building and similar sites by non-technical staff. Powers below 2 milliwatts are usually sufficient for surveying and metrology and there is normally no optical hazard (see also section 6.3). Further improvements in 'ruggedized' construction, simplified operation, and reduced prices are likely to occur. The areas of application of helium–neon lasers are likely to increase particularly with the introduction of commercial or domestic applications of lasers.

4.5.2 Helium–cadmium Laser action has been observed in various metal vapours including cadmium, selenium, and zinc.[23] Of these the helium–cadmium laser has been most extensively developed. The helium–cadmium metal vapour laser is capable of continuous wave outputs of the order of 10 mW at $0 \cdot 325 \, \mu m$ and 50 mW at $0 \cdot 442 \, \mu m$ at the ultraviolet and blue end of the spectrum. Excitation is by a high voltage d.c. gas discharge with an overall efficiency of about $0 \cdot 05$ per cent.

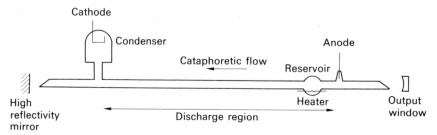

Fig. 4.13 Helium–cadmium laser

The construction of the helium–cadmium laser is shown in Fig. 4.13 and is similar to the helium–neon laser except for the addition of the reservoir and condenser. The cadmium is derived from the heated reservoir, cataphoresis in the d.c. discharge causes the cadmium to migrate towards the cathode where it condenses.[24] The migration can be reversed if a symmetrical system is used by reversing the electrode polarity. An alternative method of construction eliminates the need for a heater to vaporize the cadmium by using a segmented tube which enables the cadmium to be more uniformly distributed during operation.

The short output wavelength from the helium–cadmium laser in the ultraviolet may be suitable for chemical reactions and cross-linking and curing processes.

4.5.3 Carbon dioxide The carbon dioxide laser is representative of the large number of molecular lasers and has been extensively reviewed.[25] The carbon dioxide laser is normally excited by a glow discharge between axial electrodes using cold cathode emission in a similar way to the helium–neon laser. Induction coupled r.f. excitation has also been used. The cavity walls are normally water-cooled borosilicate tubing but a metal tube has been used at a lower specific power output.[26]

The lower transition level is close to the ground state which together with the ease of excitation of the vibration rotation spectrum of molecular lasers contributes to an overall high efficiency typically of about 18 per cent. A large number of possible transitions exists over the band 9 μm–11 μm with a mean value around 10·6 μm.

The gain of axial flow and sealed CO_2 lasers is dependent on the gas mixture, tube diameter, and current. The power output is proportional to the length and is about 50 W/m–100 W/m for axial flow lasers and 30 W/m for sealed tube lasers. The laser gas is a mixture of 6 per cent carbon dioxide, 12 per cent nitrogen, and 82 per cent helium. The minimum divergence (single mode) is about 2 milliradians.

To obtain high powers long cavities have been constructed using multiple discharges to keep the voltage required to acceptable limits. Multiple parallel folded tube constructions with single reflectors, rooftop (two surfaces) or corner cube (three surfaces) at each fold have been used to minimize the effective length. The output is normally continuous but high power pulse operation is possible and very high peak power pulses with an oscillator amplifier configuration have been obtained.

Continuous flow systems in which the gas goes to waste are used at powers below about 500 W. Recirculating and sealed systems in which a catalyst or heater reverses the dissociation reaction are used at higher powers and gas flow rates.

CO_2 lasers with sealed tubes with mean continuous ratings of up to 60 W at 8 per cent conversion efficiency and tube lives of thousands of hours (5–15) and pulsed powers of 100 W are obtainable commercially. The maximum CW power output is likely to be limited to about 200 W due to difficulties of cooling the gas (the efficiency of the laser decreases with increase in temperature), contamination of the gas from the electrodes and tube walls and the dissociation of the carbon dioxide.

Considerable interest exists in the development of high-power CO_2 lasers which offer the possibility of very high power outputs at high efficiencies. The very high power obtained together with the general applicability to other molecular lasers warrants a brief mention of the techniques that have been used.

The output power is limited primarily by the availability of excited states which, in turn, is limited by the rate of cooling.

High specific power outputs up to several hundred W/m can be achieved with high gas flow rates over short sections of small bore tube so that high heat transfer from the gas occurs[27] and forms the basis of a compact folded construction that has been developed commercially. Advantages are the relative simplicity of design and low order mode output obtainable.

Various transverse flow systems in which rapid cooling is made possible by the fast transverse flow have been developed. In one system illustrated in Fig. 4.14 the discharge is established across the flow with the optic axis also perpendicular to the flow. This is known as the gas transport laser.[28] Specific power outputs of the order of 1 kW/m resulting in a compact construction have been obtained and the laser is available commercially. If the discharge is aligned with the optic axis, a magnetic field perpendicular to the discharge can be used to reduce drag of the discharge by the gas flow and has also been used as a method of intra-cavity scanning.[29] An alternative configuration which eliminates distortion due to aerodynamic drag of the discharge has the discharge aligned with the direction of gas flow with the optic axis of the laser cavity perpendicular to it.[30]

A transversely excited atmospheric pressure laser (TEA) using a crossed field system in which the discharge and the gas flow and optic axis are mutually perpen-

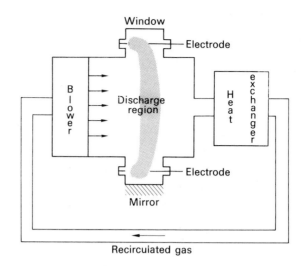

Window

Electrode

B
l
o
w
e
r

Discharge
region

Heat exchanger

Electrode

Mirror

Recirculated gas

Fig. 4.14 Transverse flow laser

dicular has been used for high-power pulsed operation of around 100 MW and high repetition rates up to 100 pulses/s corresponding to a mean power output of about 80 W/m[24] and is also available commercially.

A gas dynamic CO_2 laser using rapid expansion through a supersonic nozzle to de-populate the lower levels to achieve a population inversion has been described.[32] Power outputs up to 60 kW have been achieved using a carbon monoxide/air mixture as a fuel in an unstable cavity 800 mm long at flow rates of 13·7 kg/s at a speed of 1300 m/s. Potential power outputs of more than 1 MW have been predicted.

A further development is the electric mixing laser in which nitrogen and helium are excited in an electric discharge and carbon dioxide added downstream. This is capable of power outputs of 900 W from a cavity of effective length 0·3 m with an efficiency of 11 per cent.[33] However, the difficulty of separating the carbon dioxide from the other gases prevents recirculation of the gas.

Many advances have occurred recently in CO_2 laser technology and considerable development is still required in this area before the results can be exploited industrially. Sealed tube lasers will probably be used up to about 50 W. For medium powers up to about 1 kW the present type of low pressure high and low velocity axial flow laser will probably become standard and for high powers in excess of 1 kW, one or more of the alternative types of high power lasers still in the process of development are likely to be used.

4.5.4 Argon The argon ion laser normally uses a d.c. discharge at currents of around 10–100 A corresponding to region F–G of the discharge characteristic to excite laser action, although induction-coupled r.f. discharges have been used. The voltages used are relatively low compared with glow discharges and operation from a rectified power frequency source at line supply voltage is possible. Saturable reactors or semi-conductors are normally used to reduce excessive power dissipation in the stabilizing circuit at the high level of input power required.

The construction of a typical argon ion laser is shown in Fig. 4.15. At laser powers below about 1 W quartz tubes have been used but at higher powers the laser tube, which has to withstand very high temperatures, is made up of segmented beryllia (BeO) or graphite rings. Brewster windows with external dielectric coated optics are used to obtain a high reflectivity at the short output wavelength. An axial magnetic field of about 0·05 T stabilizes the d.c. discharge on the tube axis.

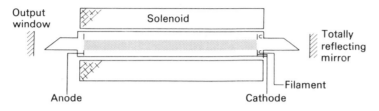

Fig. 4.15 *Argon ion laser*

Cathode erosion is severe at high current limiting the tube life. Cold and heated (thermionic) cathodes have been used. The use of a plasma jet as the cathode is reported to be more robust and result in reduced contamination in a demountable argon laser capable of very high output powers.[34]

The optimum pressure increases as the tube diameter decreases, lying between about 0·05 torr at 10 mm and 0·5 torr at 1 mm. The gas discharge results in a pressure gradient along the tube and to equalize this a parallel tube is connected between the electrodes.

Output over a range of wavelengths of 0·458 μm and 0·515 μm at power outputs up to several watts at about 0·05 per cent overall efficiency can be obtained at lengths of about 2·2 m and lasers with outputs up to 10 W are commercially available. Tuning can be achieved by intra-cavity wavelength selection. Power outputs in excess of 150 W have been achieved.[35] The beam divergence angle is about 0·5–1 milliradian.

Krypton with an output at lower powers than argon over the range 0·468 μm to 0·676 μm may be substituted for argon. Some of the wavelengths and power obtainable are also listed in table 4.5. A mixture of argon and krypton has been used with output intensity and wavelengths such that a white light output is achieved.[36]

Although the power output at present from commercially available argon ion lasers is relatively low compared with CO_2 and neodymium-doped laser material, the short wavelength enables the beam to be focused to a very small size so that very high power densities can be achieved.

4.6 Dye lasers

The efficient fluorescence of many organic compounds makes them suitable as laser materials.[37,38] Tunable outputs continuously variable over a wide range of wavelengths can be obtained at high powers. Table 4.6 summarizes the principal properties of dye lasers which have been extensively reviewed.[39]

Lasers including CW argon and pulsed nitrogen can be used to excite dye lasers but in some cases excitation is also possible with flash tubes. Overall efficiencies are about 0·1 per cent using flash tubes but efficiencies of nearly 30 per cent of conversion of the output from the pumping laser are obtainable.

Table 4.5 *Typical output wavelengths and power obtainable from an ion laser with a nominal 3 W CW output (courtesy Coherent Radiation Inc.)*

Wavelength (µm)	Gas		
	argon	krypton	mixed gas
350·7–356·4	—	100	
351·1–363·8	100		
454·5	85		
457·9	200		30
465·8	75		
468·0		5	
472·7	110		
476·2		50	
476·5	450		100
482·5		30	20
488·0	1000		250
496·5	400		70
501·7	200		40
514·5	1400		250
520·8		70	100
528·7	150		
530·9		200	80
568·2		150	D100
647·1		500	250
676·4		120	30
752·5		100	
793·1–799·3		30	

* Relative powers vary with excitation level.

Laser cavities are shown in Fig. 4.16 for excitation with a nitrogen laser and flash tube using an elliptical cavity with Brewster windows to give a polarized output in similar configurations to solid-state lasers.

An important feature of the dye laser is the ease with which the output wavelength dyes can be tuned using a grating, etalon, or acousto-optic filter over a large part of the visible wavelength. Continuous operation of tunable dye lasers over the range 0·55 µm to 0·65 µm has been achieved using an argon laser as a pumping source.[40]

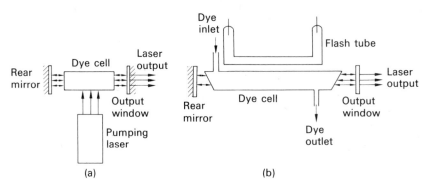

Fig. 4.16 *Dye laser cavities:* (a) *laser pumped;* (b) *pumped by a flash tube*

Table 4.6 *Summary of dye laser properties (reprinted from Bass, M., Deutsch, T. F. and Weber, M. J., 'Dye Lasers', chapter 3, 269–345 in* Lasers, *Vol. 3, Ed. A. K. Levine and A. J. De Maria, courtesy of Marcel Dekker Inc., New York, 1971)*

Property	Typical Values	Conditions	Comments
Wavelength	$3\cdot4$–$11\cdot75\,\mu$m	Flashlamp and/or laser pumped	A variety of dye-solvent combinations are available to span the entire wavelength range nearly continuously
Tuning	Up to $4 \times 10^{-2}\,\mu$m	Prism, filter, grating, Q switch in cavity	Length, concentration, and temperature of active medium also provide tuning
Spectral width	$1\cdot5 \times 10^{-3}$–$1\cdot5 \times 10^{-2}\,\mu$m	Broadband mirrors	
	$\sim 5 \times 10^{-3}\,\mu$m	Grating in cavity	
	$\sim 1 \times 10^{-4}\,\mu$m	Grating plus etalon	
Beam divergence	2–5 mrad	Flashlamp and/or laser pumped	Dependent on uniformity of pumping
	0·5 mrad	Etalon in cavity	
Efficiency	Up to 25 per cent	Laser pumped	Measured optical efficiency
	$\sim 0\cdot4$ per cent	Flashlamp pumped	Electrical energy input to laser energy output
Output			
Energy	2 J (high)–0·1 J (typical)	Flashlamp pumped	
Power	~ 2 MW	20 MW pump	Rhodamine 6G
	0·75–2·0 MW	Flashlamp pumped	
Repetition rate	Up to 200 pulses/s	Laser pumped	Pump laser rate limits
	20–50 pulses/s	Linear flashlamp	System cooling and component failure are limits
	1 pulse/s	Annular flashlamp	
Temporal			
Pulse duration	~ 20 ns	Laser pumped	Follows pump pulse
	0·5 μs typical; up to 140 μs achieved	Flashlamp pumped	Shorter than pump duration
Mode locked		Mode-locked pump	Pump cavity length integral multiple of dye cavity
	Pulses $< 10^{-9}$ s	Flashlamp pumped with intracavity saturable absorber	
	Pulses $< 10^{-11}$ s	Mode-locked pump	Observed by two-photon fluorescence

4.7 Semiconductor lasers

Various semiconductor materials have been shown to exhibit laser properties when an electric field is applied.[41,42] These are sometimes referred to as injection lasers. Some of the materials are listed in table 4.7[43] together with their output wavelength and the method of excitation used. It is also possible to combine two semiconductor materials to give an output at intermediate wavelengths depending on their relative proportions. The relative compositions are indicated by the subscripts x and $(1-x)$.

The most extensively studied semiconductor material is gallium arsenide (GaAs)[44] for which laser action can be obtained at room temperature. Electrodes are attached to opposite faces of the material and are connected to a continuous or pulsed power supply. Low-inductance circuits may be used to achieve high current pulses and rapid modulation.

Table 4.7 *Spectral range covered by semiconductor lasers (from Geusic, J. E., Bridges, W. B. and Pankove, J. I., 'Coherent Optical Sources for Communications',* Proc. IEEE, *58 (10), 1419–1439, 1970)*

	λ (μm)	$h\nu$(eV)	Excitation*			
ZnS	0·33	3·8	O	E		
ZnO	0·37	3·4		E		
$Zn_{1-x}Cd_xS$	0·49–0·32	2·5–3·82	O			
ZnSe	0·46	2·7		E		
‡CdS	0·49	2·5	O	E		
ZnTe	0·53	2·3		E		
GaSe	0·59	2·1		E		
$CdSe_{1-x}S_x$	0·49–0·68	2·5–1·8	O	E†		
$CdSe_{0.95}S_{0.05}$	0·675	1·8		E		
CdSe	0·675	1·8	O	E		
‡$Al_{1-x}Ga_xAs$	0·63–0·90	2·0–1·4			I	
‡$GaAs_{1-x}P_x$	0·61–0·90	2·0–1·4		E	I	
CdTe	0·785	1·6		E		
‡GaAs	0·83–0·91**	1·50–1·38	O	E	I	A
InP	0·91	1·36			I	A
$GaAs_{1-x}Sb_x$	0·9–1·5	1·4–0·83			I	
$CdSnP_2$	1·01	1·25		E		
$InAs_{1-x}P_x$	0·9–3·2	1·4–3·9			I	
$InAs_{0.94}P_{0.06}$	0·942	1·32			I	
$InAs_{0.51}P_{0.49}$	1·6	0·78			I	
GaSb	1·55	0·80		E	I	
$In_{1-x}Ga_xAs$	0·85–3·1	1·45–3·1			I	
$In_{0.65}Ga_{0.35}As$	1·77	0·70			I	
$In_{0.75}Ga_{0.25}As$	2·07	0·60			I	
Cd_3P_2	2·1	0·58	O			
InAs	3·1	0·39	O	E	I	
$InAs_{1-x}Sb_x$	3·1–5·4	0·39–0·23			I	
$InAs_{0.98}Sb_{0.02}$	3·19	0·39			I	
$Cd_{1-x}Hg_xTe$	3–15	0·41–0·08	O	E		
$Cd_{0.32}Hg_{0.68}Te$	3·8	0·33	O			
Te	3·72	0·334		E		
PbS	4·3	0·29		E		
InSb	5·2	0·236	O	E	I	A
PbTe	6·5	0·19		E	I	
$PbS_{1-x}Se_x$	3·9–8·5	0·32–0·146		E	I	
PbSe	8·5	0·146		E	I	
$Pb_{1-x}Sn_xTe$	6–28	0·209–0·045			I	
PbSnSe	8–31·2	0·155–0·040			I	

*A Avalanche breakdown.
  O Optical pumping.
  E Electron beam pumping.
  I Injection.
†Boldface indicates possible mode of excitation.
**Depending on temperature and doping.
‡Pulsed operation at room temperature.

A schematic illustration of a semiconductor laser is shown in Fig. 4.17. Light emission occurs from faces in the plane perpendicular to that of the electrodes. One pair of parallel sides are cleaved and may be ground and polished or even coated to increase their reflectivity while the other pair are roughened to suppress reflection from the faces.

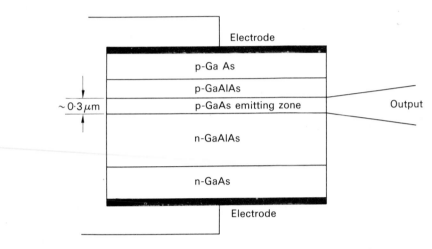

Fig. 4.17 *Double heterojunction injection laser*

The output from a semiconductor laser extends over a wide range of wavelengths since the energy transitions are poorly defined because electron transitions are between energy bands and not between discrete energy levels. Excitation is normally carried out by pulses of current which result in temperature fluctuations. Continuous operation, is however, possible in some cases if very efficient cooling is used and operation of GaAs lasers is possible at room temperature at reduced output.

Since the active region of the junction is only of the order of $2\,\mu m$ wide, diffraction results in a divergence of the order of $7°$. In the plane of the active region which is about 0.1 mm long, the effect of diffraction is smaller. The efficiency of semiconductor lasers is in excess of 10 per cent.

Improved operating efficiency at lower current densities is obtainable with a multi-layer [(AlGa)-Al-Ga-As] heterojunction within $1–2\,\mu m$ of the p–n junction but at lower peak powers than GaAs alone. The current density can be reduced with a second heterojunction on the other side. The power output is further reduced.

Typical operating conditions at room temperatures are a pulsed output power of 24 W at a pulse duration of $0.2\,\mu s$ and a repetition frequency of 1000 pps are obtained at a forward current of 60 A and a forward voltage of 8.5 V. The maximum output power duty factor pulse length and repetition frequency are very much greater at $77°$K.

The 'spin-flip' magneto–Raman laser is a continuously tunable semiconductor laser.[45] An infrared laser is used to stimulate Raman scattering in a semiconductor crystal such as indium antimonide. The crystal is situated in a high magnetic field. The conduction band electrons in the crystal can be thought of as spinning about an axis in the direction of the magnetic field. The electrons can be excited from a low to a higher energy state by reversal of their direction. Incident photons result in reversal of the spin of the electron and excitation by an amount proportional to the strength of the applied magnetic field so that the input is tunable.

Semiconductor lasers are already finding application in such areas as range-finding and pollution detection. The wide range of wavelengths obtainable, inherent simplicity of large-scale manufacture comparable to that of a transistor, compatibility with electronic circuitry, and small size can be expected to result in large-scale applications where the high divergence is acceptable.

4.8 Other lasers

The principal lasers obtainable commercially have been described. Various other lasers with potentially useful characteristics are available and are described here together with other recent developments.

The transversely excited xenon laser is also available commercially and enables high pulsed output powers of the order of 10^3 W over the range 0·49 μm to 0·54 μm to be obtained and is capable of being focused to a diffraction limited beam diameter of around 5 μm.[46] Applications are in trimming thick and thin films. A pulsed xenon laser with output in the infrared using transverse excitation in a mixture of helium and xenon with a peak output of 1000 W over the range 2 μm to 3·7 μm has been made and gives an average output power of 5 W from a length of 0·8 m.

Nitrogen lasers with high intensity-pulsed outputs at 0·337 μm have been studied[47] and are commercially available. Uses are for exciting pulsed dye lasers for holography, and Raman spectroscopy. Excitation is from a transverse pulsed electric discharge.

New developments in carbon monoxide lasers whose output lies between 5·4 μm and 6·1 μm at room temperature with various additive gases have enabled power outputs comparable with those from low-velocity axial discharge CO_2 lasers at similar efficiencies to be obtained.[48] A sealed tube CO laser with an output of 10 W with a length of 1·1 m and a CW gas dynamic CO laser have also been developed.

A selenium–hydrogen metal vapour laser with an output band of 24 lines over the range 0·498 μm to 0·531 μm with a combined output of 30 mW on 6 lines of similar design to a helium–neon laser and suitable for applications in spectroscopy is being developed.[23]

Erbium-doped hosts similar to those used for neodymium are being investigated. Principal advantages result from the output wavelength at 1·54 μm which is not transmitted by the cornea and is therefore potentially less injurious to the eye than the output of neodymium lasers.[49] Possible uses are for range-finders and similar applications where the optical hazard may be unacceptable at 1·06 μm.

Inorganic liquid lasers, as distinct from organic dye lasers, are being intensively investigated. Neodymium-doped liquids including neodymium in selenium oxychloride[50] (which is acidic and toxic) and phosphorous oxychlorides[51] have been made to show laser action. Potential advantages are very high power capability due to the high rate of heat transfer possible. Less hazardous liquids are being investigated.

Alternative methods of pumping are also being considered. Laser emission from electron beam pumping has been achieved and very short wavelengths extending the output of lasers into the X-ray region may eventually be possible using these techniques. At present the shortest wavelength obtained is $0.16\,\mu m$ with various diatomic gases.[52]

Chemical lasers relying principally or solely on chemical transitions have been used to obtain laser emission which, because of the molecular transition involved, is in the infrared region of the spectrum. At present at the development stage they offer the potential of a portable high-power laser without the need for external power supplies. The pumping energy is supplied from the reaction between the gases, which may be produced first by low-power dissociation from less reactive compounds with an auxiliary power supply. The laser transition is obtained by sudden expansion of the excited gas through nozzles usually transverse to the laser cavity axis in a similar way to the gas dynamic CO_2 laser Pulse and CW output is possible. Various suitable chemical reactions exist which can also be excited by other methods including CO,[45] DF-CO_2 at $10.6\,\mu m$ and HCl, HF, and DF over the range $2.7\,\mu m$–$4\,\mu m$.[53] Chemical efficiencies of up to 15·8 per cent have been reported for an HF chemical laser.[54]

References

1. Weber, M. J., 'Insulating Crystal Lasers', *Handbook of Lasers*, pp. 371–417, Ed. R. J. Pressley, Chemical Rubber Co., Ohio, 1971.
2. Schuldt, S. B. and Aagard, R. L., 'An Analysis of Radiation Transfer by Means of Elliptical Cylinder Reflectors', *Appl. Opt.*, **2** (5), 509–513, 1963.
3. Bowness, C., 'On the Efficiency of Single and Multiple Elliptical Laser Cavities', *Appl. Opt.*, **4** (1), 103–107, 1965.
4. Levikov, S. I., 'Laser Pump Lamps', *Sov. J. Opt. Technology*, **36** (4), 570–579, 1969.
5. 1973 Laser Focus Buyers Guide (Issued with January 1973 *Laser Focus*), Advanced Technology Publications, Newtonville, Mass., 1973.
6. Oliver, J. R., 'A Comparison of Rare Gas Flashlamps', *IEEE J. Quantum Electron.*, **5** (5), 232–237, 1969.
7. Edgerton, H. E., 'Xenon Flash Lamp Design', *Advances in Quantum Electronics*, Ed. J. R. Singer, Columbia University Press, New York, 1961.
8. Evtuhov, V. and Neeland, J. K., 'Pulsed Ruby Laser', *Lasers*, pp. 1–136, Vol. 1, Ed. A. K. Levine, Edward Arnold Ltd, London, 1966.
9. Roess, D., 'Analysis of Room Temperature CW Ruby Lasers', *IEEE J. Quantum Electron.*, **2** (8), 208–214, 1966.
10. Thornton, J. R., Fountain, W. D., Flint, W. G. and Crow, T. G., 'Properties of Neodymium Laser Materials', *Appl. Opt.*, **8** (6), 1087–1102, 1969.
11. Findlay, D. and Goodwin, D. W., 'The Neodymium in YAG Laser', *Advances in Quantum Electronics*, Vol. 1, Ed. D. W. Goodwin, Academic Press, London, 1970.
12. Oliver, J. and Barnes, F. S., 'Rare-Gas Pumping Efficiencies for Neodymium Lasers', *IEEE J. Quantum Electron.*, **5** (5), 225–231, 1969.
13. Davies, M. B., Sharman, P. and Wright, J. K., 'Comparison of the Performance of Krypton and Xenon Filled Flashtubes for Pumping Nd^{3+} Doped YAG Lasers', *IEEE J. Quantum Electron.*, **4** (6), 424–425, 1968.
14. Read, T. B., 'The CW Pumping of YAG:Nd^{3+} by Water Cooled Krypton Arcs', *Appl. Phys. Lett.*, **9** (9), 342–344, 1966.
15. Liberman, I., Larson, D. A. and Church, C. H., 'Efficient Nd:YAG CW Lasers using Alkali Additive Lamp', *IEEE J. Quantum Electron.*, **5** (5), 238–241, 1969.

16. Koechner, W., DeBenedictis, L. C., Matovich, E. and Mevers, G. E., 'Characteristic and Performance of High-Power CW Krypton Arc Lamp for Nd:YAG Laser Pumping', *IEEE J. Quantum Electron.*, **8** (3), 310–316, 1972.

17. Young, C. G., 'Glass Lasers', *Proc. IEEE*, **57** (7), 1267–1289, 1969.

18. Koester, C. J. and Snitzer, E., 'Amplification in a Fiber Laser', *Appl. Opt.*, **3** (10), 1182–1186, 1964.

19. Chester, R. B., 'A Stabilizing Sleeve for the Nd:YAG Laser', *Appl. Opt.*, **9** (9), 2190–2191, 1970.

20. Sinclair, D. C. and Bell, W. E., *Gas Laser Technology*, Holt, Rinehart & Winston, New York, 1969.

21. Bloom, A. L., *Gas Lasers*, John Wiley, New York, 1968.

22. Allen, L. and Jones, D. G. C., *Principles of Gas Lasers*, Butterworths, London, 1967.

23. Silfvast, W. T., 'New C.W., Metal-Vapor Laser Transitions in Cd, Sn and Zn', *Appl. Phys. Lett.*, **15** (1), 23–25, 1969.

24. Goldsborough, J. P., 'Stable Long Life CW Excitation of Helium Cadmium Lasers by d.c. Cataphoresis', *Appl. Phys. Lett.*, **15** (6), 159–161, 1969.

25. Tyte, D. C., 'Carbon Dioxide Lasers', *Advances in Quantum Electronics*, Vol. 1, Ed. D. W. Goodwin, Academic Press, London, 1970.

26. Avivi, P. and Dotheen-Deutsch, F., 'A Metal-Tube Gas Laser', *J. Phys. E.*, **3**, 750, 1970.

27. Tyte, D. C., 'A Compact 20 W CO_2 Laser', *J. Phys. E.*, **3**, 734–735, 1970.

28. Tiffany, W. B., Targ, R. and Foster, J. D., 'Kilowatt CO_2 Gas-Transport Laser', *Appl. Phys. Lett.*, **15** (3), 91–93, 1969.

29. Freiberg, R. J., Chenausky, P. P., and Wayne, R. J., 'Magnetic Stabilization of the Plasma Column in Flowing Molecular Lasers', *Proc. IEEE*, **59** (4), 659–667, 1971.

30. Eckberth, A. C. and Davis, J. W., 'The Cross-Beam Electric-Discharge Convection Laser', *IEEE J. Quantum Electron.*, **8** (2), 139–144, 1972.

31. Beaulieu, A. J., 'High Peak Power Gas Lasers', *Proc. IEEE*, **59** (4), 667–674, 1971.

32. Gerry, E. T., 'Gasdynamic Lasers', *IEEE Spectrum*, **7** (11), 51–58, 1970.

33. Brown, C. O., 'High-Power CO_2 Electric Discharge Mixing Laser', *Appl. Phys. Lett.*, **17** (9), 388–391, 1970.

34. Maitland, A., 'A Plasma Jet as Cathode for an Argon Laser', *J. Phys. D.*, **2**, 535–539, 1969.

35. Seelig, W. H. and Bause, K. V., 'Argon Laser Emits 150 Watts C-W', *Laser Focus*, **6** (8), 33–37, 1970.

36. Leonard, E. T., Yaffee, M. A. and Billman, K. W., 'White Light Laser', *Appl. Opt.*, **9** (5), 1209, 1970.

37. Sorokin, P., 'Organic Lasers', *Scientific American*, **220** (2), 30–40, 1969.

38. Snavely, B. B., 'Dye Lasers', *SPIE Journal*, **8** (4), 119–125, 1970.

39. Bass, M., Deutsch, R. F. and Weber, M. J., 'Dye Lasers', *Lasers*, Vol. 3, chapter 3, pp. 269–345, Eds. A. K. Levine and A. J. DeMaria, Marcel Dekker, New York, 1971.

40. 'Continuous Dye Laser Yields Tunable Output', *Physics Today*, **24** (1), 19, 1971.

41. Rieck, H., *Semi-conductor Lasers*, Ed. D. G. C. Jones, Macdonald, London, 1970.

42. D'Asaro, L. A. and Ripper, J. E., 'Junction Lasers', *Physics Today*, **24** (3), 42–48, 1971.

43. Geusic, J. E., Bridges, W. B. and Pankove, J. I., 'Coherent Optical Sources for Communications', *Proc. IEEE*, **58** (10), 1419–1439, 1970.

44. Gooch, C. H. (Ed.), *Gallium Arsenide Lasers*, Wiley-Interscience, London, 1969.

45. Shaw, E. D., 'The Spin Flip Laser', *Phys. Bull.*, **22**, 389–390, 1971.

46. Targ, R. and Sasnett, M. W., 'High-Repetition-Rate Xenon Laser with Transverse Excitation', *IEEE J. Quantum Electron.*, **8** (2), 166–169, 1972.

47. Leonard, D. A., 'Saturation of the Molecular Nitrogen Second Positive Laser Transition', *Appl. Phys. Lett.*, **7** (1), 4–6, 1968.

48. Bhaumik, M. L., 'High Efficiency CO Laser at Room Temperature', *Appl. Phys. Lett.*, **17** (5), 188, 1970.

49. 'Keep an Eye on Erbium', *Laser Focus*, **7** (1), 32–33, 1971.
50. Watson, W., Reich, S., Lempicki, A. and Lech, J., 'A Circulating-Liquid Laser System', *IEEE J. Quantum Electron.*, **4** (11), 842–849, 1968.
51. Hongyo, M., Sasaki, T., Nagao, Y., Heda, K. and Yamanaka, C., 'High-Power Nd^{3+} $POCl_3$ Liquid Laser System', *IEEE J. Quantum Electron.*, **8** (2), 192–196, 1972.
52. Hodgson, R. T., 'Vacuum-Ultraviolet Laser Action Observed in the Lyman Bands of Molecular Hydrogen', *Phys. Rev. Lett.*, **25** (8), 494–497, 1970.
53. Cool, T. A., Stephens, R. R. and Shirley, J. A., 'HCl, HF and DF Partially Inverted CW Chemical Lasers', *J. Appl. Phys.*, **41** (10), 4038–4050, 1970.
54. Mitels, H. and Spencer, D. J., 'Power and Efficiency of a Continuous HF Chemical Laser', *IEEE J. Quantum Electron.*, **7** (11), 501–507, 1971.

5

INDUSTRIAL LASER APPLICATIONS

Despite the cynical tag of a solution looking for a problem lasers are in use today in a tremendous variety of applications.

The purpose of this chapter is to include all the applications that have been carried out with lasers, with emphasis primarily on industrial applications. Present, future, and speculative applications are summarized in table 5.1. For completeness a brief treatment of communications, biomedical, and scientific applications is also given.

Many claims have been made of industrial laser applications and it is normally impossible to assess their justification without an intimate knowledge of both the technical and economic factors of the processes involved, which are often difficult to obtain. Many processes are also described that can only be assessed on technical and economic grounds for a specific application. For this reason a critical treatment of many applications is not always possible or even desirable. Whenever possible further references have been given for the benefit of those who have an intimate knowledge of their specific requirements and are in a better position to assess the usefulness of lasers in their own application.

5.1 The use of lasers in metrology

Lasers, and in particular the helium–neon laser, have already found extensive application in non-contact methods of distance measurement. Principal advantages of the laser over other light sources for these applications are the monochromatic output, coherence, and low divergence, resulting in increased range of operation and greater accuracy than are obtainable by other optical methods.

The helium–neon laser is most widely used for metrology, where its visible output which is comparatively safe at low powers, its simplicity of construction, and its relatively low cost make it directly competitive with conventional light sources.

Applications in metrology tend to divide into two categories. For the first, which includes precision distance measurement by interferometric methods, a monochromatic stable coherent output is required. The second category, which includes surveying and alignment, requires only a low divergence.

Table 5.1 *Principal present and future areas of application of lasers in industry*

Areas of Application	Present Applications	Applications Under Development	Speculative Applications
Biomedical	Ophthalmology	Skin treatment, surgery, dentistry	Sterilization, agricultural applications
Electronics and electrical engineering	Sub-miniature welding, mask preparation for circuit production, resistor trimming, capacitor construction, ceramic substrate scribing	Current measurement at high voltages, computer data transmission, storage	
Communications	Communications in space, line-of-sight communication	Large display, television recording, credit-card verification, identification systems	Optical filtering, telephone transmission, satellite communication
Civil and mechanical engineering	Alignment, surveying, precision length measurement, velocity measurement, strain measurement, non-destructive testing	Gyroscopes, stress measurement, range-finders, altimeters, vibration analysis	Mining, rock cutting
Metal fabrication	Sub-miniature welding, drilling, material removal, profile cutting sheet metal	Sheet metal welding, deep penetration welding	Surface treatment
Fabrication of non-metals	Perforating, cutting plywood dies for the carton industry, piercing holes in elastomers and diamonds for wire-drawing dies, textile cutting	Glass cutting and welding, plastic cutting and welding, paper slitting	Surface treatment
Printing		Copying processes	Books, high-speed computer output.
Military	Range-finders, gun-fire simulators, surveillance, communications, missile homing	Anti-missile weapons	
Scientific	Spectroscopy, combustion studies, high-speed photography, vacuum melting, particle sizing, spark gap bridging	Controlled atomic fusion	
Miscellaneous	Vacuum melting, pollution measurement monitoring, lighthouse, cloud height monitor	Navigational aids	Underwater applications

5.1.1 Measurement of length An accurate method of measurement of distance is by interference techniques. Light from a monochromatic coherent source is divided into two beams so that reflected light from a mirror (e.g., rooftop or corner cube prism) mounted on one surface is allowed to interfere with reflected light from a second reference surface. One form of laser interferometer is shown in Fig. 5.1. The reference surface together with the beam splitter may be an integral unit which can be simply set up. The separation between the fixed reflector and the beam splitter is kept constant to within less than $\lambda/10$. As the second reflector is moved the light interferes alternately, constructively and destructively at intervals of half a wavelength of the light output used, producing variations in intensity that can be detected by a photo-electric detector and counted with a digital counter. An accuracy of $0\cdot1$ μm can be achieved but it is dependent on an accurate knowledge of the refractive index over the optical path and the instrument design tolerance.[1]

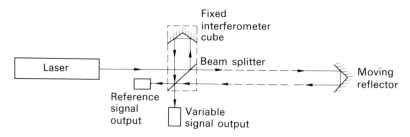

Fig. 5.1 Principle of operation of laser interferometer

The long coherence length that is obtainable from a single mode uniphase output coupled with the relatively high intensity of the monochromatic output and small divergence (<1 millirad) enables laser interferometers to be used over long distances extending the application of interference techniques using conventional light sources from about $0\cdot2$ m up to about 120 m.

The time required to make a distance measurement by interferometry is limited by the high signal-to-noise ratio of normal light sources to about 1 m in one second but measurements can be made at several metres per second with a laser interferometer, only limited by the measuring circuit response.[2] The same technique may also be used for velocity and frequency measurements if the time during which displacement occurs is measured.

A high degree of stability of the output wavelength is necessary since the distance is measured in terms of the output wavelength of the laser. A coherent output which is not always needed for other applications is also required. Helium–neon lasers are normally used in interferometers and employ special techniques in order to achieve high stability of output wavelength and coherence. Effects due to ambient light can be reduced by modulating the laser output or using a detector with a narrow band pass filter. Effects of variation in the refractive index of the air over the path length due to convection and changes in atmospheric pressure, humidity and non-uniform expansion of the structure being measured due to temperature variations limit the overall accuracy unless compensated for.

Laser interferometers are being used for calibration,[2,3] testing,[4] and measure-

Fig. 5.2 *Laser interferometer used for accurate positioning of aircraft components on a machine tool. The laser is shown in the foreground, the interferometer is in the centre of the figure. The digital readout is shown in the bottom righthand corner (courtesy Perkin Elmer Corp.)*

ment[5] of machine tools, inspection,[5,6,7] precision measurement, and for comparisons with standards. Figure 5.2 shows a laser interferometer being used to set up a work-holding fixture on a machine tool used in the production of precision aircraft components. The absence of the backlash encountered in conventional mechanical systems enables very precise location to be established not limited by the tolerance of

Plate I · *Laser interferometer being used to calibrate machine tool (courtesy Perkin-Elmer Corp.)*

lead screws. Plate I shows a laser interferometer being used for calibrating a machine tool scale.

Variation in pressure through the variation in refractive index of a fluid can be measured and an interferometric method has been developed for calibration purposes and as a dynamic pressure transducer.

Optical interference techniques using the laser as a source of parallel monochromatic light but not requiring a source with a coherent output and therefore of lower cost, have been used for various less critical applications in metrology. A method of extending the accuracy of Moiré fringe measurements from about $2\,\mu m$–$3\,\mu m$ to about $0\cdot2\,\mu m$ has been developed capable of accurate measurements over relatively short distances of the order of several hundred millimetres independently of variation in refractive index and turbulence over the path length. The optical system is shown in Fig. 5.3. The laser output, which may be incoherent, illuminates three slits at a time in the first plane which form interference fringes. The movement of the interference fringes is determined by a detector on the other side of a short length of conventional Moiré grating. The total number of slits in the first plane is governed by the length over which measurement is required. The spacing between the slits and distance of the slit to the plane of the grating depend on the wavelength of the light used. Using a

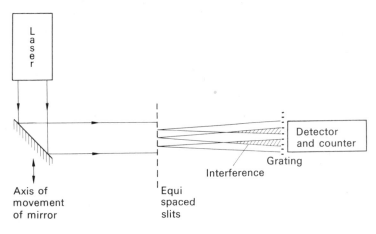

Fig. 5.3 *Length measurement by fringe counting*

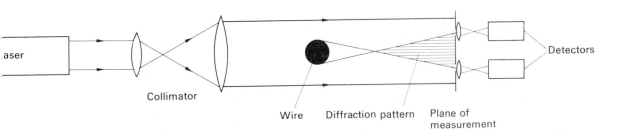

Fig. 5.4 *Gauging wire diameter from the diffraction pattern formed in a laser beam*

helium–neon laser at 0·63 μm a fringe spacing of 1 μm is obtained 1·4 mm from the slits if a slit separation of 1 mm is used.

Similar methods may also be used to determine small variation in surface smoothness or curvature from that of a reference surface, a variation showing as a distortion of the fringe pattern.

The high overall accuracy that is obtainable by interferometric methods of measurement is not required for many applications for which a high degree of coherence and stability of wavelength are not necessary. One method of measuring the diameter of thin wire uses the interference fringes resulting from diffraction of the light by the wire in the laser beam, Fig. 5.4.[9,10] The detection of a null magnified to fill the detector's aperture indicates that the wire is outside its dimensional tolerance. The system uses the change in fringes formed by diffraction with wire diameter which cause a variation in the output from the photodetector and can be used as part of a control system or warning indicator. A measure of the diameter can be obtained by moving the photodetector until the output is restored to its original value. Changes in wire diameter as small as 0·2 per cent over wire diameters from 0·005 mm to 0·20 mm can be measured.

A system for non-contact measurement of large objects to an accuracy of about

0·01 mm using the low divergence of a laser beam is shown in Fig. 5.5. A rotating mirror at the focus of the first lens produces a beam parallel to the optic axis. The time between the leading edge of the beam being extinguished by the object and when it emerges from the other side is a measure of the cross-section which is a function of the tangent of the angle subtended by the object at the focus of the first lens. The technique is being used to measure the roundness and diameter of hot steel bars under conditions of vibration to an accuracy of 0·025 mm over diameters of 5–25 mm.[11]

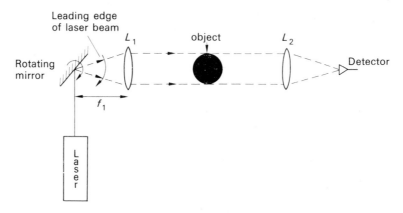

Fig. 5.5 *Laser scanning gauge*

5.1.2 Surveying and alignment The application of lasers to surveying and alignment of structures is well established. Surveying and alignment applications use the laser beam as a reference to measure the angle or deflection from the required alignment. The requirements of the optical source are less critical than those for interferometry and the principal advantages of a laser over other light sources are the low divergence and high intensity output enabling it to be used over long distances with higher definition. The intensity of the light output from a conventional collimated light source and the total energy falling on a detector decreases inversely with the square of the distance from the source. The divergence of the output of a beam from a helium–neon laser is about 1 mrad (single mode) and about 5 mrad (multimode). The divergence can be further reduced by expanding the beam with a collimator to about 50 mm diameter corresponding to a divergence of about 2×10^{-5} rad and an increase in beam diameter of about 1 mm over a path length of 300 m. Neither a coherent output nor stable output wavelength are necessary, resulting in a laser of lower cost than that required for interferometry. A low-power ($\leqslant 2$ mW) single mode helium–neon laser is normally used as the source.

A laser transit mounted on a tripod is shown in operation in Fig. 5.6. An important feature is the precise alignment of the optical axis of the laser beam with the mechanical axis of the laser mount which is normally used as a reference. The beam is expanded to a diameter of about 30 mm with a collimator which simplifies detection and location of the centre of the beam with a light-sensitive detector used as a target and also reduces the divergence.

The beam is normally visible in the transverse direction by scattering of light from

Fig. 5.6 *K. & E. Construction alignment laser in use (courtesy Keufel and Esser Co.)*

small particles in the beam. The use of suitable filters which can be incorporated in goggles (sometimes referred to as beam finders) that can be used to attenuate visible light while passing the laser light enable the scattered light to be more easily seen when the beam is viewed from the side. The power output required is below the safety threshold value (see also section 6.3) and up to now operation in an enclosed area without safety measures has been accepted.

For surveying and alignment applications a quadrant detector is normally used. One form is shown in Fig. 5.7. A vertical or horizontal deflection of the beam from the centre of the detector together with the direction is shown by the indicating meters. When the laser beam is central the two indicating meters indicate zero. Small distances from the centre of the laser beam can also be measured in this way if the meters are calibrated. If necessary the laser output may be modulated to reduce effects due to ambient light or fluctuations in refractive index due to convection. Alternatively a detector with narrow band pass filter may be used. Surveying applications in which lasers are being used include pipe laying (Fig. 5.8), level grading, dredging, long submarine pipe lines,[12] and tunnel boring.[13] Systems using a detector mounted to obtain a proportionate signal corresponding to either vertical or horizontal displacement used as a feed-back signal for correction of alignment are in use on trench digging equipment and for road surfacing.[14]

Accuracies (0·38 mm in 60 m) six times better than obtainable with a standard

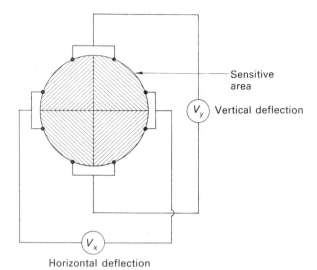

Sensitive area

V_y Vertical deflection

V_x

Horizontal deflection

Fig. 5.7 *Quadrant detector target for centring laser beam*

Fig. 5.8 *Laser mounted in manhole for aligning pipe during pipe laying (courtesy Jodon Engineering Associates Inc.)*

alignment telescope optical method are claimed, limited mainly by variations in atmospheric pressure.

The high accuracy obtainable and elimination of subjective assessment using null indicating methods or digital outputs and the need for only one operator are of particular value in the alignment of large mechanical structures. As well as a reference line the laser may also be rotated about an axis to generate a reference plane for such applications as dredging and the alignment of large structures.[15] By mounting the axis of a laser vertically and using a pool of mercury to support the totally reflecting mirror very accurate vertical alignment is possible.[16]

Examples of applications of lasers in alignment of structures include alignment of aircraft wings and air frame jigs,[13,15,17] tunnelling machines,[16] linear accelerators,[13] and for positioning of ships' stern tubes, guide tubes in atomic reactors,[18] and king pins on trailer axis on long trailers.[19] A special hand-held portable helium neon laser intended for use in alignment applications in hazardous environments such as coal mines is shown in Plate II. Applications in mining include positioning girders and conveyor alignment.

Small deflections of large structures under varying load can also be measured. The

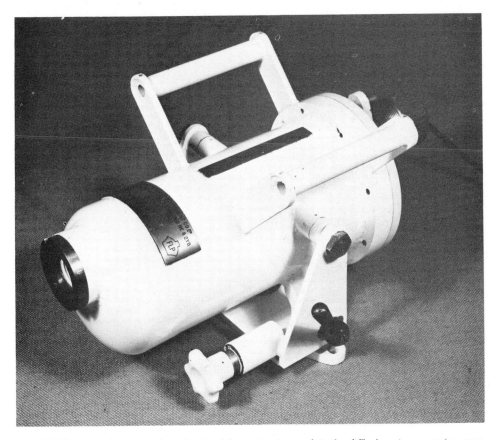

Plate II *Flame-proof alignment laser developed for use in mines and similar difficult environments (courtesy International Research and Development Co.)*

laser or the target is used as a fixed reference, mounting the other on the structure either using the meter calibration or by moving the target until a null is obtained. Alternatively a reflector may be mounted on the structure and the deflection measured from a remote location. A helium–neon laser of the type used for surveying and alignment is suitable. Applications include the deflection of the decks of oil tankers, dams, and bridges under load.

Plate III Helium-neon laser being used to align elevated crane rail track (crane in the background) (courtesy Marconi Elliott Avionic Systems Ltd.)

5.1.3 Laser range-finders and altimeters Optical range-finders use time-resolved methods to determine the transit time of a reflected pulse of light in a similar way to radar techniques. The technique is sometimes referred to as LIDAR (LIght Detection

And Ranging) by analogy with radar. Advantages of optical techniques are the security from detection (outside the visible region), the ability to reproduce an image, relative simplicity of the system, and high accuracy obtainable. Typical accuracies obtained using pulsed lasers are of the value of ± 5 m at ranges of 8–10 km.

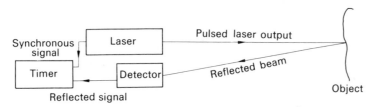

Fig. 5.9 *Principle of operation of laser range-finder*

The laser characteristics for range measurement are different from those required for spatially resolved metrology techniques. The principle of operation is illustrated in Fig. 5.9. Frequency modulation of a CW output or single or repetitive short high power pulses of low divergence are used. The duration of the pulse must be short compared with the time taken for the signal to reach the detector. Greater accuracy may be obtained using CW output with frequency modulation, eliminating the error corresponding to the delay during the rise time of the pulsed source. More than one modulating frequency can be used to eliminate ambiguity, the greatest accuracy being obtained at the highest frequency. A retroreflector can be mounted on a co-operative target such as in surveying over long distances. The phase shift of the reflected signal is compared with a reference signal reflected along a reference path of known length built into the system. Distances of over 50 miles with an accuracy of ± 6 mm have been obtained in this way using a frequency-modulated CW helium–neon laser.

High powers are required if the intensity of the reflected signal, which is normally from a diffuse reflecting surface, is small. Ruby, neodymium, erbium, and arrays of high-power injection lasers are used for pulsed range-finders. Where the use of optical range-finders is required to be concealed, as in surveillance and military applications, lasers with outputs outside the visible spectrum are sometimes necessary. Danger of retinal damage from the high pulse power of ruby and neodymium lasers and injection lasers is likely to limit their civil applications. The output of erbium lasers (1·54 μm) is less injurious to the retina due to the low transmission of the cornea at 1·54 μm so that the beam cannot be consciously focused on the retina and higher power levels may be used.

Gated viewing is used for range-finding and obstacle detection in fog and smoke and underwater, where the light scattering limits the range of detection. The operation of a gated range-finder is illustrated schematically in Fig. 5.10. The detector is switched on for a short interval after a time delay equal to the time taken for an unscattered beam to travel from the source or illuminator to the object to be viewed and return thereby eliminating the effects due to scattered light. High sensitivity detectors such as image intensifiers may be necessary due to the low intensity of the reflected beam. Scanning in depth can be carried out by varying the delay period.

Laser range-finders are now fitted as standard equipment to some armoured fighting vehicles and are being used for military surveillance. Likely civilian applications are

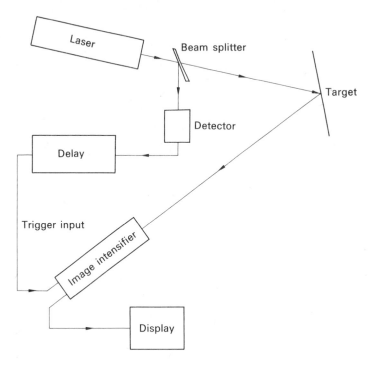

Fig. 5.10 *Gated laser range-finder*

in surveillance in crime detection, optical radar in conditions of low visibility for aeroplanes and essential service vehicles (ambulance, police cars, and fire engines) and underwater applications,[20, 21] and the use of lasers for altimeters[22] at low levels for aircraft.

The possibility of using range-finding techniques for obstacle detection as an aid for the blind is being extensively studied. A laser cane using semiconductor lasers is under evaluation and enables detection of obstacles and shallow steps.[23] An alternative system uses a gallium arsenide laser with detector mounted on a spectacle frame. If the beam is reflected from an obstacle a 100 Hz tone is heard.[24]

Laser radar systems have been used to investigate the presence of dust layers and other atmospheric constituents at heights between 40 km and 10 km which are difficult to examine by ground-based or satellite techniques.[25]

5.1.4 Measurement of velocity and position by the Doppler effect The Doppler effect is caused by relative motion between source and observer which results in an apparent change in frequency and can be applied to a wide range of velocity measurements using a low-power helium–neon laser.[26]

Where the detector and source are fixed and the beam is reflected from the target the frequency of the detected radiation is altered by

$$f = \frac{2U}{\lambda} \cos \theta$$

where f is the change in frequency, U is the velocity of target, λ is the wavelength of

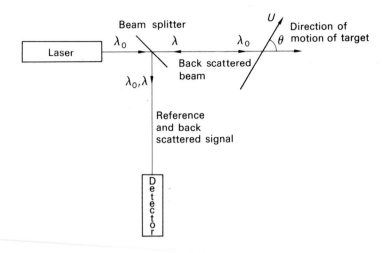

Fig. 5.11 *Principle of velocity measurement using the Doppler effect*

transmitted signal, and θ is the angle between direction of motion and of the target.

If the output wavelength and phase of the laser remain constant when the frequency of the reference and reflected or transmitted signal are added the difference in frequency can be easily and accurately determined. For example using a helium–neon laser ($\lambda = 0{\cdot}6238\,\mu\text{m}$) and with $\cos\theta = 0{\cdot}5$ a velocity of $1\,\text{m/s}$ corresponds to a difference or beat frequency of $15{\cdot}08\,\text{MHz}$. The principle of operation is illustrated in Fig. 5.11, as applied to the measurement of the velocity of transparent fluids. Pressure fluctuations in transparent fluids result in local changes in the refractive index since

$$\frac{\text{d}n}{\text{d}p} = \frac{n-1}{k}$$

where n is the refractive index, k is the constant related to the modulus of the material, and p is the pressure.

Alternatively particles or bubbles intercept the laser beam causing a small resultant change in velocity and hence a Doppler frequency shift[27,28] which can be used to measure the velocity.

Various optical arrangements are possible for the measurement of velocity by the Doppler effect, and are shown in Fig. 5.12. Two beams are obtained with a beam splitter. Similar methods obtain two beams by expanding the beam and passing it through two apertures. An equal path-length system is obtained in this way which is independent of variations in path length. Variations in refractive index with time of fluids is compensated by passing the reference beam through the fluid.

The reference-beam mode shown in Fig. 5.12(a) is used to measure the velocity of a transparent medium where the effect of scatter is high. The alignment tolerance is not critical. The differential Doppler mode (b) and (c) can be used where the intensity due to scattered light is low, and utilizes unscattered and scattered light from both beams. Higher laser powers are required using back-scattered light to measure fluid velocities. The differential Doppler mode using back-scattered light (c) can also be used for measuring the velocity of opaque objects.

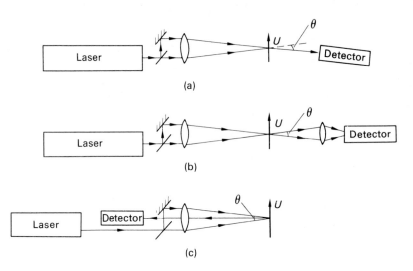

Fig. 5.12 Examples of systems used for velocity measurement using the Doppler effect: (a) reference beam mode; (b) differential Doppler-mode for forward scattered light; (c) differential Doppler mode for backward scattered light

The Doppler effect can be as a non-contact method of measuring the velocity of transparent or opaque moving rod and sheet and has been used for measuring the velocity of aluminium extrusions, hot steel strip, plastics sheet, paper, nylon fibres, and many other materials at speeds from 150 m/min down to 12 mm/min.[26] Laser Doppler techniques have been used for remote measurement of wind velocity and turbulence,[27] and wind velocities in wind tunnels.[28] Flow profiles across the diameter of a pipe and measurements of oscillating flows have also been made.[29] Optical noise produced by the laser can be reduced by combining a second signal from the output beam of the laser with a differential amplifier.

The use of laser Doppler methods is applicable to measurement of flows of fluids containing particles of dimensions down to 1 μm or where small variations in refractive index due to density changes occur (which normally exist), and for opaque objects of surface roughness above about 1 μm. Velocity measurement of opaque objects is obtained with the laser and detector both mounted on the same side of the object. Typical velocity ranges readily attained are from 10 mm/s to 4×10^4 mm/s with an

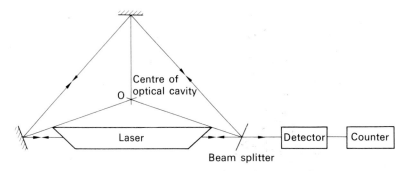

Fig. 5.13 Schematic illustration of a ring laser

accuracy of 1 per cent. Techniques have also been developed for the measurement of the vibration of rotating objects such as turbine blades.[30]

The ring laser can be used to detect small changes in angular position using the Doppler effect and can be used as a gyroscope which is virtually independent of magnetic fields.[31] Helium–neon lasers are normally used.

A ring laser is illustrated in Fig. 5.13. The shape is not important provided that it forms a closed loop which behaves as a single laser. If the laser rotates about the axis O then a difference in frequency of the light travelling in opposite directions occurs. The change in frequency

$$\Delta f = \frac{4\omega A}{\lambda l}$$

where A is the enclosed area, l is the total path length, λ is the laser wavelength, ω is the rate of rotation about axis.

$\Delta f/f$ can be readily arranged to be of the order of 10^{-6}. The change in frequency is measured by combining the two outputs at a photo-detector and determining the beat frequency which can be easily measured, 100 Hz corresponding to a rotational motion of less than the order of $0.01°/s$. Mode locking is prevented by rotating the gyroscope at an accurately known velocity.

A ring laser gyroscope is being used for detecting small variations in rail track alignment of the Bay Area Rapid Transit System in San Francisco.[32]

5.2 Laser fabrication processes

Very high power densities can be achieved by focusing the beam of a high power laser. Typical power densities obtainable from pulsed and CW lasers and other high intensity sources are listed in table 5.2.

Table 5.2 *Power densities obtainable from high-intensity sources*

Heat Source	Power Intensity W/mm^2
Blackbody radiation (3000 deg C)	6.45×10^2
Oxy-acetylene flame	10^3
Transferred arc plasma torch	10^5
Electron beam	10^9
Laser (continuous) (CO$_2$)	2.5×10^6
(pulsed) (Nd)	$> 10^{12}$

The high energy that is obtainable in the focused output of a laser beam enables the laser to be used as a source of thermal energy for such fabrication processes as melting, welding, drilling, thermal practice, and surface treatment. Some of these processes and listed in table 5.3 illustrated schematically in Fig. 5.14.

The maximum power density at the focus of the laser beam is governed by diffraction (ignoring lens aberrations) for which

$$\delta = 1.22 \, M \frac{\lambda}{F}$$

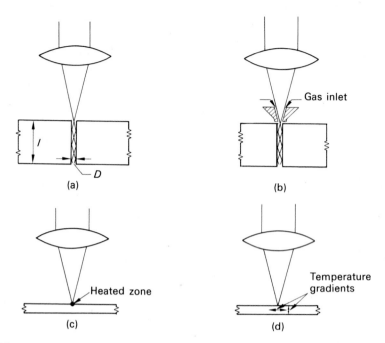

Fig. 5.14 *Fabrication processes using lasers:* (a) *drilling;* (b) *cutting with gas jet assistance;* (c) *scribing;* (d) *thermal fracture*

where δ is the diffraction limited diameter, and M is a function of the mode structure (for a single mode $M = 1$, multi-mode $M > 1$); and the power density

$$\frac{W}{A} = \frac{4W}{M^2 F^2 \lambda^2 \pi} .$$

The minimum practical value of F lies around 1, governed by workable values of aperture and focal length. In practice, while a lens of low F number is required to obtain a high power density other requirements may limit the minimum focal length that can be used. For drilling applications a hole size greater than the minimum obtainable may be needed and for welding, evaporation, and heat treatment a lower power density over a large area may be required. Of the lasers available at present only CO_2, neodymium, ruby, and argon ion lasers have sufficient power output to do more than

Table 5.3 *Fabrication processes that can be carried out with lasers*

Application	Material	Output
Line and profile cutting	Metals, plastics, glass, ceramics, textiles, composites, wood	CW
Welding	Metals, plastics, composites	Pulsed CW
Scribing	Ceramics	Pulsed CW
Drilling	Metals, ceramics, plastics	Pulsed
Melting	Refractory materials, metals, non-metals	CW
Machining operations	Metals, plastics, ceramics	Pulsed CW
Heat treatment	Metals	CW

evaporate thin films and up to now the high cost of argon ion lasers has precluded their use for fabrication processes. Neodymium and ruby lasers have been primarily used for applications requiring a pulsed output such as drilling, microwelding, scribing, and trimming. CO_2 lasers have been used for pulsed and continuous applications including scribing, cutting, and welding. Although a high-power CW output is obtainable from neodymium lasers, the limited lamp life at high powers, poor stability, low efficiency and high capital cost have up to now limited its application.

Depth of focus is important where for example parallel-sided cuts or holes are required and affects the tolerance and positioning of the workpiece at the focus. The depth of focus is derived from the divergence of a focused beam (see section 2.2) and is the distance between two points either side of the focus at which the intensity is diminished by the same amount. The depth of focus often used in optics is the distance measured between half-intensity points which, for a Gaussian energy distribution, is given by

$$z = \frac{d_0^2 \sqrt{2}}{4\lambda} 10^{-3} \ .$$

where z is the depth of focus. For many fabrication processes, this corresponds to too great a variation in power density and the depth of focus is measured between points at which the intensity is diminished by 10 per cent from that at the focus where

$$z = \frac{\pi}{12} \cdot \frac{d_0^2}{\lambda} 10^{-3}$$

The depth of focus for a CO_2 laser at 10·6 μm with a beam diameter of 10 mm is 3·48 mm. For the same beam diameter at 1·06 μm, the depth of focus is 34·8 mm, but for a beam diameter of 3 mm is reduced to 3·17 mm.

A number of different energy transfer processes take place at the interface of a laser beam at a metal surface. These include absorption, reflection, transmission, evaporation, re-radiation and thermal diffusion.[33] While the interaction of these processes makes quantitative analysis difficult, for most practical applications the absorption and power intensity together with the melting point and thermal diffusivity are most important in controlling the process. In cutting and drilling processes where an auxiliary gas jet is used, the existence of an exothermic reaction with the ambient gas can also have a dominant effect on the process.

Of the power incident at the surface some will be reflected, some absorbed, and some transmitted so that

$$W_i = W_r + W_a + W_t$$

where the subscripts refer to the incident, reflected, absorbed, and transmitted power respectively.

The attenuation of short wavelengths in metals is very high and at optical wavelengths the penetration depth of radiation from the surface at which the intensity is $1/e$ of that transmitted at the surface is normally less than 10^{-8} μm for most metals, and therefore the transmitted power can be ignored. The attenuation in non-metals is often small and has to be taken into account. The magnitude of the absorbed power density required to carry out various processes is indicated in Fig. 5.15. Below 10^2 W/mm² little or no discernible effect occurs except for very thin films, while above

10^7 W/mm^2 ionization and breakdown of air occurs. The reflectivity of the material, which varies with wavelength and temperature, and also the presence of thin films or oxide layers limits the absorbed energy at the surface.

The effect of the absorbed power in the material is governed by the thermal properties of the material (thermal conductivity, diffusivity, melting point, vaporization temperature, specific and latent heats) together with the density and geometry (which affects the thermal diffusion and conduction in the material). The heat transfer due to pulsed, Q-switched and steady-state lasers have been studied. In most fabrication processes the heat input per unit volume is most important. For material removal where vaporization takes place the heat of vaporization governs the process, but for welding the heat of fusion is important. The difference between the heat capacity at

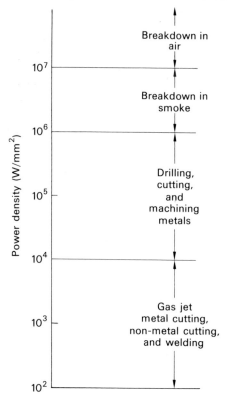

Fig. 5.15 *Power density required for different processes*

vaporization and the capacity at the boiling point of the material is an important criterion for welding processes, a large difference implying a greater tolerance to power variation.

In drilling and some welding processes the maximum power that can be used is limited by explosive ejection of material and formation of vapour above the material. At very high powers formation of plasma may also occur. Vapour and plasma formation tends to deform the laser beam and reduce its effectiveness.

The absorption mechanism for metals has been examined and appears to be critically dependent on a threshold value of power density.[34] For pure metals the absorption apparently increases due to oxide formation above a critical temperature. In the case of alloys preferential evaporation of the constituents with the lowest melting point below the boiling point for the alloy, results in a rapid increase in absorption and evaporation and oxidation.

5.2.1 The drilling process Lasers may be used for drilling by vaporization of material at the focus of the beam. The drilling process has been extensively studied.[35,36,37,38] A laser and optical system suitable for drilling, microwelding, and fabrication of microelectronic components is shown in Fig. 5.16. Continuous observation is possible

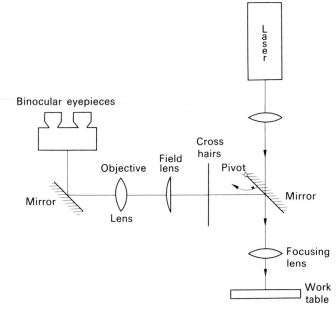

Fig. 5.16 *Laser and associated optics for drilling, microwelding, and fabrication of micro-electronic circuits*

if a beam splitter is used instead of a pivoted mirror and if filters are inserted between the eyepiece and the beam splitter to prevent transmission of reflected laser power through the eyepiece. A laser microprobe is shown in Fig. 5.17 and forms the basis for drilling and welding systems.

The energy supplied for drilling should be such that rapid evaporation of material takes place before significant radial diffusion of heat into the workpiece occurs, so limiting melting and the heat affected zone to the region adjacent to the hole. The maximum power density and the pulse length are limited by excessive vaporization above the hole and at high powers the formation of a plasma plume which results in absorption of the laser energy in the vapour rather than the material.

The drilling mechanism may be assisted in some cases by maintaining a positive pressure on the front face of the workpiece such as with a gas jet or with a low-pressure chamber on the reverse side of the workpiece to assist removal of vaporized material and dross at breakthrough.[39] The gas jet also has the additional advantage of preventing vapour condensing on the lens. A photo-detector positioned a safe distance below the material can be used to determine when penetration has occurred.

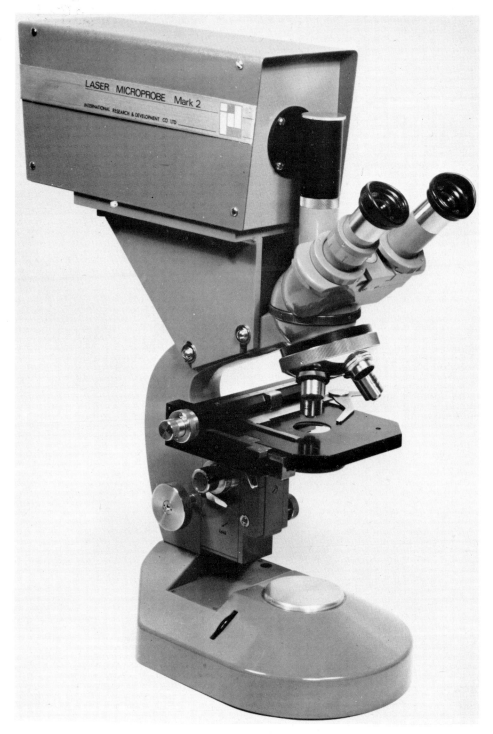

Fig. 5.17 *Laser microprobe using ruby or neodymium glass laser (courtesy International Research and Development Co.)*

Holes with high aspect ratios (l/D where l is the thickness of the work and D is the hole diameter) as high as $20:1$[40] can be obtained due to the aperturing effect of the hole at the focus and multiple reflection from the side walls of the hole (Fig. 5.14).

The use of a series of pulses minimizes the energy diffused laterally into the workpiece and assists in controlling the hole size and shape. Pulse durations of the order of milliseconds are required to enable sufficient thermal diffusion along the axis of the hole to occur rather than only absorption at the surface. Where the metallurgical requirements are critical the use of high power pulses of short duration thereby minimizing thermal diffusion are preferable to reduce the effect of re-solidification of melted material on the sides of the hole.[41] Holes other than circular can also be produced by apertures in the focused beam or before the lens. Apertures within the laser cavity can be used but are more complex to design although often more efficient.

Table 5.4 *Parameters for laser drilling (from Moorhead, A. J., 'Laser Welding and Drilling Applications', Weld. J., 50 (2). 97–106, 1971)*

Material		Laser Parameters		Hole Diameter (mm)	
Type	Thickness (mm)	Pulse Length (ms)	Energy Output (joules)	Entrance	Exit
PE Magnesium	0·157	1·8	2·1	0·036	0·020
PE Magnesium	0·157	2·0	3·2	0·041	0·031
Molybdenum	0·051	2·0	3·3	0·025	0·020
Molybdenum	0·051	2·25	4·9	0·025	0·020
Molybdenum	0·051	2·35	5·9	0·025	0·025
Copper	0·081	2·25	4·9	0·020	a
Type 304 stainless steel	0·091	2·35	5·9	0·051	0·025
Tantalum	0·157	2·35	5·9[b]	0·031	0·015
Tantalum	0·157	2·42[c]	8·0[c]	0·031	0·010
Ti–6% Al–4% V	0·244	2·35	5·9	0·041	0·015
Ti–6% Al–4% V	0·244	2·4	7·0	0·046	0·015
Ti–6% Al–4% V	0·244	2·4	7·0[b]	0·051	0·051
Tungsten	0·051	2·0	3·3	0·020	0·015
Tungsten	0·051	2·1	4·0	0·020	0·020
Tungsten	0·051	2·35	5·9	0·025	0·031

A 94·8 mm objective lens was used in each case with the beam sharply focused at the surface. One laser pulse was used for each hole except where noted.
[a] Not measured.
[b] Two laser pulses.
[c] Extrapolated value.

Some of the drilling parameters using a pulsed ruby laser to drill a variety of metals are listed in Table 5.4.[42] Maximum thickness of materials that can be drilled is about 2·5 mm with hole diameter ratios of up to $20:1$ using several pulses. Pulsed ruby and neodymium lasers are being used for drilling holes of small aspect ratio in hard metals which are difficult to drill by other methods. Applications include cooling holes in turbine blades and spinneret plates used in the manufacture of artificial fibres.

The use of a CO_2 laser to drill holes in stainless steel in and out of vacuum has been studied in detail.[38] The threshold value of power for drilling was three times greater in a vacuum due to the higher emissivity of the stainless steel in vacuum. Analysis of the heat transfer was made and a nomograph enabling the critical power P_m or the time for melting to occur after onset of heating the target obtained. A thermal analysis of the drilling process in alumina has been made and was in agreement with experimental results obtained with pulsed ruby and CO_2 lasers. Where hole symmetry is important repetitive pulsing combined with rotation of the workpiece to reduce the effect of non-uniformity in the focused beam is used. Large holes may be produced by rotating the work eccentrically about the optical axis in a similar way to trepanning. Axicon lenses which use aspherical lenses to produce an off-axis focus have also been used to produce holes of larger diameter than the focused beam in non-metallic materials.[43]

Pulsed lasers have also been used to balance small rotating parts by metal removal. Watch balance wheels 0·1 mm thick have been balanced dynamically with a split beam from a pulsed Nd:YAG laser by drilling holes 0·1–0·7 mm diameter simultaneously from opposite sides of the wheel.[44] A system for automatically balancing small components using a pulsed ruby laser is illustrated in Fig. 5.18.[35] Deflection of the laser beam is synchronized with the rotation of the component so as to allow a longer pulse duration and hence more material to be removed than would otherwise be possible. The trigger signal for the laser is derived automatically from the vibration pick-ups on the shaft.

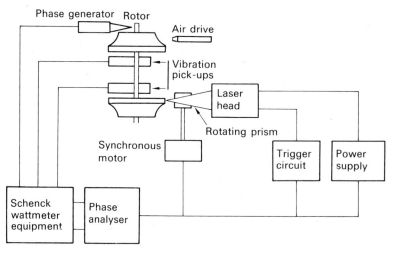

Fig. 5.18 *Laser balancing machine (from Scott, B. F. and Hodgett, D. L., 'Pulsed Solid State Lasers for Engineering Fabrication Processes', Proc. Inst. Mech. Engrs., **183**, Part 3D, 75–84, 1968–1969*

A pulsed neodymium and glass laser with an output of 2 J is used for trimming mercury-in-glass thermometers by vaporization of the column at a pre-set position, causing the column to separate. Another established application is the use of ruby and neodymium lasers for roughing out and re-sizing diamond dies used for wire drawing.[45] Final polishing is carried out by conventional abrasion techniques. Power levels of up to 1·5 J per pulse at up to 10 pulses per second of about 200 μs duration are used. Hole sizes less than 0·025 mm can be obtained. Multiple pulsing combined with rotation of the diamond results in satisfactory hole symmetry. By off-setting the axis of rotation of the diamond from the axis of the laser beam large diameter holes can be bored in a similar way to a trepanning action. Considerable saving in time and reduction in use of the diamond grinding paste previously necessary are obtained. Watch jewels can also be drilled in this way and the process is in use in production applications. Similar techniques are employed to remove flaws due to black spot impurities in diamonds.

Although many non-metals are easy to drill, lasers have some advantages where high speeds and small holes, particularly in elastomeric materials, are required.

Plastics nozzles for aerosol cans have been perforated and the sprues from injection moulded parts have been removed using lasers.[47] (The same reference also describes the use of an axicon lens for cutting large holes in plastics.) Nylon buttons have been perforated, eliminating the production of particles by mechanical drilling methods and irregular edges which catch on thread used to attach them, causing breakage.[46] Elastomeric materials, because they readily deform, are difficult to perforate by normal methods. The use of a CO_2 laser to drill a large number of small holes in plastics[47] and thin rubber sheet using an aluminium mask and co-axial gas jet has been described.[48] CO_2 lasers are also being used to perforate teats for babies' bottles. These are difficult to drill due to the tendency of the material to deform during drilling, which results in the production of irregular-shaped holes.[49] Three holes are drilled simultaneously using a three-way beam splitter.

5.2.2 The cutting process

The cutting process is essentially one of material removal from the cut or kerf except in the case of thermal fracture. For cutting, a CW or pulsed output with a repetition frequency such that a series of overlapping holes results, is required to produce a continuous cut. The kerf width should normally be as small as possible without re-welding of the material taking place. This applies principally to plastics and can be taken as less than 0·025 mm.

The effectiveness of a laser for cutting can be increased by the use of a gas jet co-axial with the laser beam[50] and has been extensively used with CO_2 lasers.[51]

The effect of the gas jet on the depth of cut and cut speed has been studied for Perspex.[52] The depth of cut increases as the pressure is increased until a value of pressure is reached (about 2–3 bar) when further increase in pressure has no further effect. The cutting rate was largely independent of the gas used and gas pressure where the material does not react exothermically with the cutting gas. Cooling of the top surface of the material also occurs, resulting in a square cut edge. Even materials that burn in air, such as paper, can be cut, since the cooling effect outside the focus is normally large enough to prevent burning outside this region. Deep parallel-sided cuts of high aspect ratios depending on the properties of the material can be obtained in excess of the depth of focus.

A typical gas jet system for cutting is shown in Fig. 5.19. The nozzle outlet is located in the region of the focus and is larger but comparable with the diameter of the focused beam.

Parallel cuts greater than 50 mm deep have been obtained in wood, and over 150 mm deep in foamed polystyrene. The deep, parallel cuts are due to aperturing the most effective part of the laser beam at the surface of the material, multiple reflections at the cut sides as shown in Fig. 5.14 and the effect of the gas jet vapour and particles in the slot.

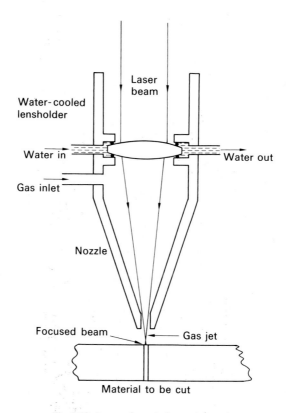

Fig. 5.19 *Lens and nozzle for gas jet cutting*

The gas jet also assists in removing vapour and particles which might otherwise condense in the cut region or on the focusing lens.

Some of the non-metallic materials that have been cut with CO_2 lasers are shown in table 5.5.[53] The cutting rates quoted are not unique inasmuch as they depend on the parameters of the laser optics, power and mode structure of the laser output. The maximum cutting speed using gas jet assistance increases approximately proportionally with the laser power for a given thickness of material. Non-metallic materials that are difficult to cut with the power levels available at present are those which vaporize at high temperatures, such as compressed asbestos, stone (marble, granite, etc.), and graphite and silicon carbide both of which also have a high reflectivity over the infrared and visible region.

Most wood products can be effectively cut by a CO_2 laser with gas jet assistance, and parallel cuts up to 50 mm deep have been obtained in deal, and cutting rates of 50 mm × 100 mm section wood at 19·8 m/min have been reported.[55] Hard woods cut at slower speeds due to their greater density and higher thermal conductivity. The maximum cutting rate decreases as the density and the moisture content increase, but is virtually independent of grain direction.[56]

Some typical cutting rates for various thicknesses of plywood are shown in Fig. 5.20. Carbonization of the cut edge occurs but it is normally limited to a very shallow region within about 50 μm of the surface; the effect is little more than a discolouration

Table 5.5 *Some representative results of cutting rates for non-metallic materials with a CO_2 laser with gas jet assistance (after Harry, J. E. and Lunau, F. W., 'Electrothermal Cutting Processes using a CO_2 Laser', IEEE Trans. Industry Applications, **8** (4), 418–424, 1972)*

Material	Thickness (mm)	Power (W)	Gas	Cutting Rate (mm/min)
Asbestos				
Compressed	6·4	180	Air	762
Cement	6·4	335	Air	25
Ceramics				
Aluminium oxide	0·75	100	none*	1500
Confectionery				
Wafer biscuit (9 layers)	27	250	Air	1000
Oatmeal biscuit	6	260	Air	1500
Glasses				
Soda Lime	2	350	Air	750
Quartz	2	250	none*	95
Ruby	0·4	100	none*	2000
Paper				
Matt	0·33	60	Air	28 800
Gloss	0·33	60	Air	40 000
Plastics				
Acrylic	3·1	300	Air	1830
Polyvinyl chloride	3·2	300	Air	3600
Expanded polystyrene	20	300	Air	10
Textiles				
Nylon	—	180	Air	3600
Vinyl (36 stack)	—	330	Air	25
Leather	3	225	Air	3050
Wood				
Oak	16	300	Air	279
Deal	50	200	Air	125
Hardboard	3·8	300	Air	910
Plywood	4·8	350	Air	5300

*Thermal fracture

and decreases with increase in cutting speed.[56] Plate IV shows a CO_2 laser cutting 18 mm plywood with gas-jet assistance.

Satisfactory cutting of composite wood products such as plywood, chipboard, and hardboard depends largely on the bonding adhesive used. Composites using urea formaldehyde cut easily with little charring but melamine and phenolic bonded composites char excessively in most cases.

One of the first viable industrial applications of CO_2 lasers has been for cutting precision slots in plywood used for steel rule dies for pressing out cartons in the packaging industry.[57,58] More recent applications include cutting the wooden dies used for cutting out fabric linings for cars and gaskets both of which are in use in the automobile industry in America. The slots in the dies are used to hold the knives for cutting and inserting crease lines during the manufacture of cartons. Important requirements are a high accuracy and constant cut width together with a high degree

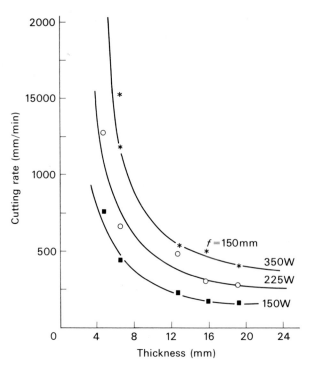

Fig. 5.20 *Variation of cutting rate with thickness for plywood with a CO_2 laser and gas jet assistance (air) (from Harry, J. E. and Lunau, F. W., 'Electrothermal Processes using a CO_2 Laser', IEEE Trans. Industry Applications, **8** (4), 418–424, 1972*

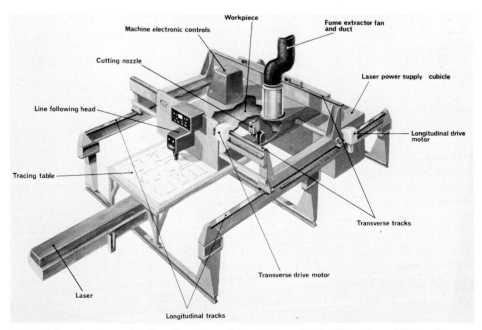

Fig. 5.21 *Laser Die Cutting Machine (from Harry, J. E. and Lunau, F. W., 'Electrothermal Cutting Processes using a CO_2 Laser', IEEE Trans. Industry Applications, **8** (4), 418–424, 1972*

Plate IV CO_2 *laser shown cutting wood with gas jet assistance (courtesy Coherent Radiation Inc.)*

of parallelism of the cut since the knives are held only by friction. An automated process of high accuracy is made possible by the non-contact cutting process which is not affected by non-uniformities in the plywood.

A die cutting machine is illustrated in Fig. 5.21 uses a 200 W multi-mode CO_2 laser.[57] The workpiece (a sheet of up to 1·65 m × 1·14 m, 18 mm thick plywood) is guided by an optical line follower over the stationary laser which cuts upwards. At least seven installations of which three use numerical control to move the wooden forme are in use in industry in Europe and the U.S.A.

Paper and cardboard can be slit at high speeds using CO_2 lasers. The cut speed is largely independent of surface finish decreasing with material thickness. Stack cutting is also possible. A limited amount of carbonization at the cut edge occurs at slow speeds, but is not apparent at high cut speeds. An important advantage over existing mechanical methods of slitting are the absence of broken fibres which remain attached due to electrostatic attraction and interfere with the printing process. Sandpaper has been cut at 305 m/min and corrugated paper can be cut without crushing the corrugations and cutting speeds of 107 m/min have been reported.[55] The eventual development of an industrial system for cutting paper or board largely depends on the availability of a high-power single- or low-order mode CO_2 laser with an output power of several kilowatts.

Most thermoplastics can be cut satisfactorily with a CO_2 laser[46,61,62] cutting rates

123

using a 300 W laser with gas jet assistance have been measured for various plastics.[63] Good-quality cut edges are obtainable, although some degradation occurs with temperature sensitive plastics such as PVC; acrylic sheet and polypropylene can be cut with a cut-edge approaching optical quality. CO_2 lasers are also being used for selective removal of insulation from delicate wire by evaporation, the wire is unaffected because of its high reflectivity. Another industrial application is the stripping of high temperature outer insulation of co-axial cables.[63]

Textiles can be cut in single layers at speeds comparable to thin films and polyester carpeting has also been cut. Some fusing at the edges occurs which reduces fraying. Stack cutting is possible, but edge-welding occurs between layers of artificial fibres at the cut edge in the same way as plastic film, the cutting gas tends to permeate sideways between the layers of material resulting in an irregular cut width and penetration of vaporized material. This can be eliminated by compressing the stack either by using vacuum suction from below or by using a ring of gas jets co-axial with the main cutting jet which compresses the stack and results in a gas flow towards the cut.

Considerable interest in the use of CO_2 lasers for cutting textiles in the tailoring industry has been shown. The cut edge of a typical man's suit is about 20 m. Several single lay laser cutting systems using mirrors to steer the laser-beam by numerical control for cutting 'off the peg' men's suits are in operation in U.S.A.[66] The same reference also describes other automated methods. The cutting system uses a computer to interpolate between standard sizes and patterns of men's suits which are then cut at speeds up to 7·5 m/min with a 200 W CO_2 laser with gas jet assistance. The principal advantage claimed is the rapid turn-round time which is not possible by conventional tailoring methods and which enables inventories at tailors' shops to be reduced while improving the service.[67] The cutting head and table are shown in plate V.

The cutting of laminate and other composite materials deserves special mention. In laminated structures such as plastic, steel, and fibre composites the relatively slow cutting speed governed by one of the materials tends to result in degradation of the other material in the cut region. The presence of non-uniformities including voids results in disturbance of the gas jet and a non-uniform kerf is formed. The use of higher power lasers capable of higher cut speeds reduces both these effects extending laser applications to composite materials that are difficult to cut by normal methods. Boron–epoxy composites 8·1 mm thick have been cut successfully at 1650 mm/min and fibre glass composites up to 12·6 mm thick at 2540 mm/min at a laser power of 16 kW.[68]

Brittle materials such as ceramics and glasses can be cut by scribing followed by mechanical fracture. Only a small amount of material is removed from the top surface of the material during the scribing process. A gas jet is not required and a pulsed output can be used.[69] Fracture is obtained by flexing the material mechanically after scribing. Considerably lower power densities than those for cutting are needed and the heat affected zone is small.

The use of a CO_2 laser for cutting brittle materials such as glass and alumina by controlled thermal fracture is possible.[70, 71] The high absorption of the laser beam at the surface of the sheet (Fig. 5.14) results in high local thermal stresses causing fracture. High cutting speeds are readily achieved. The process is surprisingly controllable, the fracture following the path of the beam, provided external effects such as convection due to draughts are eliminated.

Plate V *Numerically controlled computerized system for cutting tailors patterns using a CO_2 laser (courtesy English American Tailoring Co.)*

Glass can also be cut with a CO_2 laser using gas jet assistance, and welded. Quartz can be cut and several installations are in use for cutting quartz tubes.[63] Quartz can also be welded with a high degree of precision and the effect of heat close to the weld is minimized.[72]

Glass and ceramic materials such as zirconium oxide have been melted to produce spheres[73] and cuts and grooves in a variety of ceramics have been machined and engraved by removing material by evaporation.[73, 74] Grooves suitable for resistance heater windings have been produced in this way.

Although the absorption of most metals is low at the output wavelength of the CO_2 laser the cutting effectiveness of a CO_2 laser is quite high for ferrous metals, titanium, and other metals which react exothermically with the cutting gas. High cutting rates are achieved in this way at moderate values of laser power which would otherwise be insufficient to remove the volume of the material in the kerf. Films of the edge during cutting mild and stainless steel show the formation of molten oxide and striations at the cut edge.[75, 76] These are dependent on the cut speed and when the exothermic reaction proceeds at a greater rate than the mean cut speed an intermittent cutting action results.

An initial threshold level of power is required to initiate the cut which is dependent on the rate of thermal diffusion from the cut region and hence geometry of the material. The threshold level is also dependent on the presence of oxide films. Absorbent coatings have been used to reduce the threshold of materials of high reflectivity. Absorption of metals is high in the near-infrared and the high power CW YAG laser which because of its shorter wavelength is also capable of being focused to a smaller beam diameter is potentially suitable for metal fabrication processes. Up to now, however, no application work on YAG lasers has been reported at powers sufficient to cut reasonable metal thicknesses (>0.5 mm) and the limited lamp life and multi-mode CW output obtained at high powers are likely to limit its application in industry. Applications of argon ion lasers have been limited to thin films.[73]

Table 5.6 *Summary of typical cutting rates for metals (CO_2 laser with gas jet assistance)*

Material	Thickness (mm)	Speed (mm/min)	Power (W)	Gas	Reference
Mild steel	0.76	508	150	Air	78
	1.8	635	200	O_2	78
	2.3	1800	850	O_2	75
	2.84	889	350	O_2	78
Stainless steel	0.3	4320	350	O_2	53
	3.25	229	350	O_2	53
	5.0	780	850	O_2	75
	8.0	360	850	O_2	75
	12.5	225	3800	CO_2	79
	9.3	1524	16000		80
	44.3	381	16000		80
Aluminium 2219 alloy	6	30	3800	CO_2	79
	12.5	2540	16000		80
Nimonic 90 alloy	1.25	2280	850	O_2	75
Nimonic 90 alloy	1.42	610	250	O_2	78
Nimonic 75 alloy	0.79	406	225	O_2	53
Nimonic 75 alloy	0.7	2040	850	O_2	75
Nimonic 80A alloy	0.7	4500	850	O_2	75
Titanium (pure)	0.51	1540	135	O_2	78
	25.4	3810	16000	—	80
Titanium TA115 alloy	0.91	4820	225	O_2	53
Titanium 6A14UA alloy	2.24	3810	210	O_2	78
Titanium alloy	5.0	3300	850	O_2	75

A considerable amount of data on cutting rates of sheet metals by multi-mode CO_2 lasers exists and some representative results are listed in table 5.6, but there are scarcely any data for single-mode CO_2 lasers. There is considerable discrepancy between the results obtained because of the different cutting conditions used, in particular variations in the focal length of the lenses used, nozzle design, and assessment of cut speed, which can be based on the maximum cutting rate or optimum cut quality.

Results of tests carried out under controlled conditions for stainless steel, and where the maximum cutting rate has been obtained as a function of material thickness and laser power, are shown in Fig. 5.22.

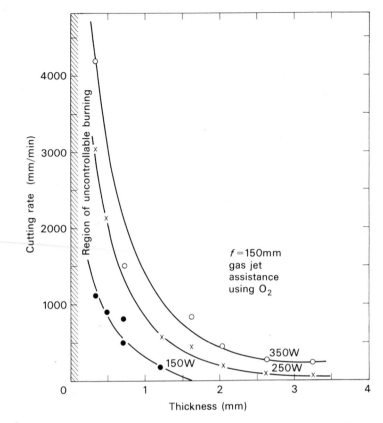

Fig. 5.22 *Variation of cutting rate with thickness and power for stainless steel with a CO_2 laser and gas jet assistance (from Harry, J. E. and Lunau, F. W., 'Electrothermal Processes using a CO_2 Laser', IEEE Trans. Industry Applications, **8** (4), 418–424, 1972)*

A potential application is for cutting sheet metal below about 6 mm thickness such as mild steel, stainless steel, nickel alloys, and titanium. The main area of application is in the aircraft and automobile industries. The use of laser cutting is particularly attractive for cutting airframe and sheet metal used for engine exhaust podding when the limited number of components required precludes the use of dies and many of the materials used are difficult to cut by conventional methods. A related area of application is for cutting and trimming three-dimensional pressings used for jet exhaust systems and for cutting out damaged areas of engine chambers. Many of these applications are already in the course of development or in limited application in the aircraft industries.

A 500 W CO_2 laser system using a moving laser guided by a line follower has been developed for profile cutting and is shown in Fig. 5.23.[81] The principal area of application is for cutting stainless steel sheet below 6 mm thickness above which plasma cutting is normally used but causes buckling of thinner sheet.

5.2.3 Welding There are two principal types of weld, conduction limited and deep penetration. These are illustrated in Fig. 5.24. The depth-to-width ratio of the weld

Fig. 5.23 *400 W multifold CO$_2$ laser mounted on the carriage of a line follower profile cutting machine in use cutting stainless steel with gas jet assistance (courtesy Ferranti Ltd)*

zone is about 3:1 for conduction limited welds and 10:1 or more for deep penetration welds. Pulse and CW lasers have been used for conduction limited welding in which the depth of the welded zone is limited by thermal conduction from the top surface. Conduction limited welds are characterized by the heat-affected zone (HAZ) either side of the weld which is large compared with the actual weld depth.

A high degree of stability of the laser output is necessary for repeatable weld quality

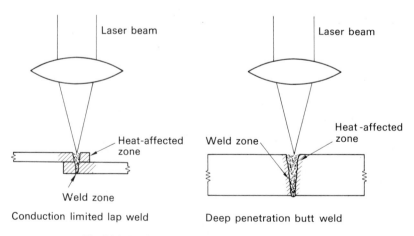

Fig. 5.24 *Conduction limited and deep penetration welds*

128

to be achieved. The absorption of most metals increases with temperature and is higher in the molten and vapour phases than the solid phase. As a result an unstable state is easily reached. The effect of varying geometry on the heat dissipation also affects the welding conditions. Variation in the laser output power and mode structure, particularly of pulsed lasers, due to internal heating and fluctuations in the output of the discharge tubes used to excite solid-state lasers, all result in variation in the welding conditions.

Some measure of the ease of weldability of metals is obtained from the ratio of the energy required to completely melt the material from the solid phase at the melting point over the energy required to reach the melting point.

Neodymium lasers are normally preferred to ruby lasers as the longer pulse length obtainable enables greater overall heat transfer to take place without excessive vaporization. Some results for welds obtained with a pulsed neodymium laser at $1.06\,\mu m$ are listed in table 5.7. An analysis of the thermal conditions in pulsed welds has been made, together with some actual laser welds, and metallurgical analysis of the weld zone and adjacent areas.[82] A portable laser welder is shown in plate VI.

A comparison of plasma arc, tungsten inert gas (TIG), electron beam, and a pulsed ruby laser used to weld a support tab on a machined cylinder has been made.[41] The laser weld produced the least distortion A tube was brazed to a thin-walled cylinder

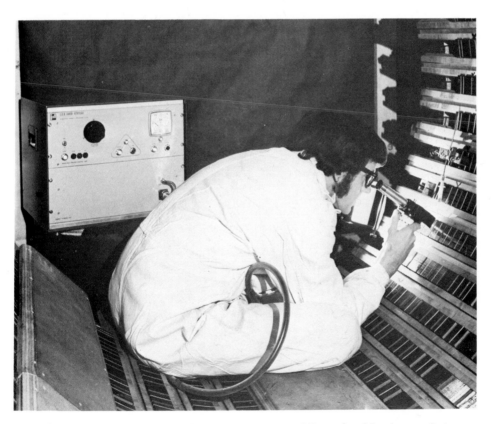

Plate VI *Portable ruby laser welder (courtesy International Research and Development Co.)*

Fig. 5.25 *Ruby laser welding system.* (a) *Automatic welding machine for welding contact blades of miniature relays at a production rate of 1000/h. Two lasers are used and each beam is divided into two.* (b) *Simultaneous welding at three points on a beryllium-copper coupling wheel of an automatic Omega watch; diameter of weld 0·2 mm, magnification 20 × (courtesy Alcyon Electronique et Physique SA)*

Table 5.7 *Examples of welds obtained with a pulsed neodymium glass laser output 0–25 J, pulse length 0·5–10 ms (courtesy Laser Inc.)*

Material to Material	Range of Thickness (mm)	Material to Material	Range of Thickness (mm)
406 Aluminium–406 Aluminium	0·0254 to 0·508	Nickel–Copper	0·025 to 1·524
Cold Roll–Cold Roll	0·127 to 2·54	Nickel–Nickel	0·025 to 0·762
Copper–Moly–Nickel	0·025 to 0·254	Stainless–Copper	0·051 to 1·702
Gold–Aluminium	0·0127 to 0·762	302 Stainless–302 Stainless	0·025 to 2·54
Gold–Gold	0·0127 to 0·762	Stainless–Tantalum	0·025 to 0·762
Inconel–Inconel	0·127 to 1·016	Tantalum–Nickel	0·0127 to 0·508
Kovar–Aluminium	0·025 to 0·508	Tungsten–Molybdenum	0·0127 to 0·508
Kovar–Copper	0·0127 to 0·762	Tungsten–Copper	0·0127 to 0·508
Kovar–Kovar	0·051 to 0·508	Tungsten–Nickel	0·0127 to 0·508
Molybdenum–Molybdenum	0·025 to 0·508	Tungsten–Platinum	0·0127 to 0·381
Molybdenum–Titanium	0·0127 to 0·635	Tungsten–Tungsten	0·0127 to 0·812
Nickel-Chrome–Molybdenum	0·051 to 2·54	Zircaloy 4–Zircaloy 4	0·025 to 1·702

with a ruby laser. The laser weld resulted in negligible carbide precipitation. Other examples include the welding of a capsule containing a temperature-sensitive indicator and welding various thermocouples to a variety of materials. Pseudo-welds in which the tops of locating pins or rivets or a screw thread are melted and flow to form a mechanical bond to hold the part in place have also been used.

Lasers offer various advantages for continuous welding processes comparable with those obtainable by electron beam processes. A good bead finish is achieved because of lack of disturbing effects on the weld normally obtained with arc processes. Good fatigue properties are obtained because of the lack of undercut which occurs with electron beam processes. (This is probably due to the ability to use a shielding gas which permits enough oxidation to give a low surface tension at the bottom face of the weld.) The heating mechanism is simpler and more controllable than arc or electron beam welding processes. Since wavelength of the radiation is of one value only, feedback of weld condition may be much easier because of the ease with which the impinging radiation may be filtered out and prevented from interfering with the sensor, enabling adaptation to automated welding processes. It is less demanding in the matter of access to the weld region than is an arc welding torch. As a vacuum chamber is not required it is readily adaptable to continuous throughputs and large structures.

Conduction welding in foils and thin sheet is obtainable[83, 84, 85] with CO_2 lasers and an example is shown in Fig. 5.26(a). A weld region wider than its depth is formed. Various metals have been welded with CO_2 lasers. Some examples of continuous welds using a 250 W CO_2 laser with argon shield gas are given in table 5.8.[83]

CW CO_2 lasers have been used for deep penetration welding in which heat is transferred along the depth of the weld producing a weld bead that is deeper than it is wide. An example of a deep penetration weld produced with a CO_2 laser at 1·6 kW is shown in Fig. 5.26(b). No filler material is normally used. A close fit between the surface to be welded is desirable; however, satisfactory butt welds have been achieved with a mean separation of 0·5 mm in 6 mm stainless steel at a laser power of 8 kW with an aberration-limited beam diameter of 1 mm. A co-axial shielding jet of a suitable inert

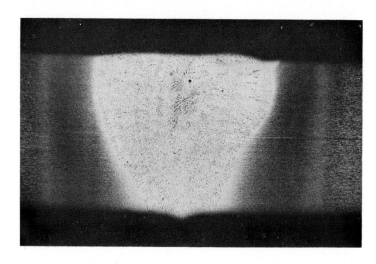

Fig. 5.26 *Cross-sections of conduction and deep penetration welds obtained with a CW CO_2 laser at a power level of 1·6 kW: (a) Conduction limited weld in 4·4 mm martensitic stainless steel made at 123 mm/min; (b) Deep penetration weld in 2 mm stainless steel made at 1500 mm/min (courtesy Welding Institute)*

Table 5.8 *Conduction limited welds made with a CW CO_2 laser at 250 W (after 'CO$_2$ Laser Joins the Parade', Welding Engineer, 55 (8), 42–44, 1970)*

Material	Weld Type	Thickness (mm)	Rate (mm/min)	Weld Width (mm)
Stainless steel (321)	Butt	0·25	889	0·71
Stainless steel (302)	Butt	0·25	250	1·01
Inconel (600)	Butt	0·25	1000	0·46
Monel (400)	Butt	0·25	381	0·64
Comm. pure titanium	Butt	0·25	1270	0·56
Stainless steel (302)	Lap fillet	0·25	381	0·76

gas can be used when air is to be excluded. Butt welds in up to 2·4 mm thick nickel alloys have been produced with a 700 W laser at about 25 mm/min comparable with those obtainable by electron beam welding with penetration ratios of 6:1.[86] Deep penetration welds with aspect ratios of 10:1 comparable with those obtainable by electron beam welding have been achieved at power levels of several kilowatts in low-carbon steel and stainless steel up to 20 mm thick and are listed in table 5.9.

Table 5.9 *Deep penetration welds produced with CW CO_2 lasers*

Material	Weld Type	Thickness (mm)	Rate (mm/min)	Laser Power (kW)	Reference
Stainless Steel (302)	Butt	6	1270	3·5	88
(302)	Butt	3	574	3·5	88
(304)	Butt	7·5	381	3·5	88
(304)	Butt	20	1270	20	87
(304)	Butt	13	2540	20	87
(304)	Butt	9	760	8	87
(1010)	Coach	1	3810	3·9	87
	Fillet	1	3040	3·9	79
Stainless steel	Butt	18	508	16	80
Stainless steel	Butt	12·5	1270	16	80
Stainless steel	Butt	6	5080	16	80
Stainless steel	Butt	1·5	8890	16	80
Titanium	Butt	4·5	5080	16	80

The application of metal welding processes has up to now been limited by the availability of high-power CW lasers. There is a lower limit to weld bead size and hence laser power due to the necessity to cater for lack of fit-up always found in practice. In general weld beads of 1 mm width are required.

At powers of about 8 kW ionization occurs in the vapour cloud above the workpiece which absorbs most of the incident radiation preventing it from reaching the target. The vapour jet can be easily removed with an ancillary gas jet.

The high surface absorption at 10·6 μm of plastics also makes the CO_2 laser attractive as a potential welding source for thermoplastics. Many plastics which can be welded by conventional thermal methods may be welded in sheet or film form with a CO_2 laser. A prism-shaped reflector enables both surfaces to be heated simultaneously.[89]

5.2.4 Laser beam profile following systems Relative motion between the laser and workpiece is required in most fabrication processes. One method is to move the work, keeping the laser and laser beam stationary. This is particularly suited to in-line continuous trimming processes in which the direction of the cut required is the same as the work movement (Fig. 5.27(a)). A profile can be followed by moving the laser or the laser beam in a direction transverse to the movement of the work.

The workpiece can be moved in both *x* and *y* directions to follow a profile (Fig. 5.27(b)). This is used in the carton die cutting machine shown in Fig. 5.21. The inertia of the workpiece limits the maximum speed and the intricacy of the profile that can be

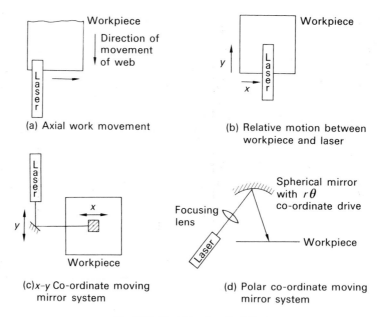

(a) Axial work movement

(b) Relative motion between workpiece and laser

(c) x–y Co-ordinate moving mirror system

(d) Polar co-ordinate moving mirror system

Fig. 5.27 *Methods of profile following*

followed. Typically, to follow a 2 mm radius arc the maximum speed is limited to about 10 m/min. A disadvantage of the moving work system is the large floor space required for large workpieces.

An alternative method is to move the laser with respect to the work as in the metal profile cutting machine in Fig. 5.23. This also suffers from limited accuracy and relatively low speed of operation due to high inertia and is limited to compact laser designs.

Moving mirror systems, Fig. 5.27(c) may be used to provide relative movement between the beam and the workpiece on one or two axes. A high degree of precision and rigidity is required due to the optical lever effect. Variations in path length and hence beam diameter at lens optics result in variations in size and power density at the focus and constant path length systems may be necessary. Two plain mirrors may be used to deflect the beam in x and y co-ordinates or a single spherical mirror of long focal length can be used to deflect the beam using a lens between the mirror and the laser to retain the beam in focus at the surface of the workpiece. (Fig. 5.27(d).) A spherical mirror with a long focal length comparable with half the maximum dimensions of the workpiece is necessary. The beam is held automatically in focus as it traverses the workpiece by the lens system which is coupled to the mirror movement.

Various methods may be used to programme the relative movement between the laser and the workpiece depending on the application. Manual methods may be used for low throughout applications; more often, however, automated processes are required in order to make the most effective use of the laser.

For repetitive drilling, pulsed welding, and applications in microelectronics, numerical control systems are normally used. Advantages over other methods include compatibility with other numerical control systems and flexibility of programming. Point-to-point systems are normally sufficient.

For cutting and continuous welding applications and some applications in microelectronics such as scribing, continuous path control systems are necessary and operation at constant speed is required to obtain a uniform cut width and heat-affected zone.

Straight-line and arc-of-circle numerical control systems can be used for contours which can be approximated by simple geometrical profiles. However, for more complex irregular profiles continuous path systems are necessary. The maximum operating speed is governed by the complexity of the contour and the size of the computing facility of the system. Operating speeds higher than those obtainable by line followers can be achieved and accuracy of position to within less than 0·025 mm is obtainable.

Optical line followers using a photo-detector can be used to follow line drawings of the cut path (Fig. 5.21). Scaling up or down can be achieved with a pantograph system. Following accuracy within 0·125 mm is sufficient for many applications. A second signal can be obtained by differentiating between thick and thin lines.[57] Such a system can be used for cutting intricate profiles at constant speeds in which continuous cuts are not required and without run-in from the side of the sheet. Alternatively it may be used for a point-to-point system. Line follower speeds of the order of 10 m/min are obtainable. The maximum speed is governed by the inertia of the system and the minimum radius that it is required to follow without overshoot.

5.3 Application of lasers in the manufacture of electronic components

The applications described here are essentially similar to those of fabrication processes described in section 5.2. The scale and other common features justifies their separate treatment.

The electrical and electronics industries in which the laser was initially developed have been among the first to utilize lasers in production applications.

Up to now the principal application of lasers in the manufacture of electronic components has been during stages of manufacture of thick and thin film components and integrated circuits, and equipment is in widespread use for a variety of production applications. The small intensely heated zone has been used for cutting, welding, and controlled evaporation during manufacture of micro-circuits and integrated circuits using laser systems similar to that shown in Fig. 5.16. Contact-free operation, ease of automation, accuracy of positioning, and high throughput obtainable are some of the advantages achieved.

5.3.1 Scribing and perforation of substrates
An application in which lasers are being extensively used is for perforating and dividing silicon slices on which there may be several hundred integrated circuits.[69, 70, 71] The use of a laser to cut the silicon substrate is likely to cause overheating and damage to the circuit but laser scribing followed by fracture by flexing enables a low power input to be used, minimizing heat transfer to the circuit itself. (See also section 5.2.2.)

The scribing action uses a focused pulsed laser beam to produce a series of shallow depressions on the top surface of the ceramic substrate[69] shown between each circuit in Fig. 5.28. The pulsed action minimizes thermal stresses in the substrate and over-heating of adjacent components. The CO_2 laser is suitable because of the high absorption of non-metallics at 10·6 μm and low power sealed CO_2 lasers have been used.

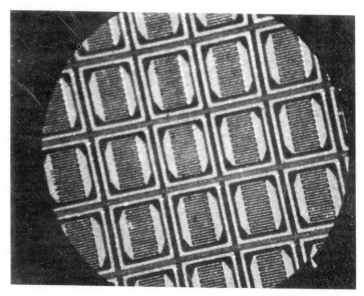

Fig. 5.28 *Thin film resistors on a 0·15 mm thick silicon wafer cut at 150 mm/s using acousto-optic Q-switched Nd:YAG laser at 3000 pps (courtesy Holobeam Inc.)*

Single-mode operation is necessary to obtain a sufficiently small diameter focused beam. The CO_2 laser may also be used to scribe substrates used for thick and thin film circuits. Power outputs of 50 W at 10·6 μm have been used to scribe 0·625 mm thick alumina at over 3 m/min.

An alternative process which has been developed and which may also be applicable to silicon substrates is the use of controlled thermal fracture[70,71] in the same way as glass, which is also described in section 5.2.2. Again, the high absorption of non-metallics at 10·6 μm makes the CO_2 laser most suitable.

Lasers have been used to perforate substrates after the deposition phase enabling more precise location of the holes to be achieved. Holes in alumina used for thin film substrates 0·7 mm thick and 0·125 mm to 0·3 mm diameter have been produced with a single pulse per hole using a 250 W CW CO_2 laser in a pulsed mode. A vacuum chamber behind the substrate to assist removal of fused material was used together with gas jet assistance.[34]

5.3.2 Trimming applications Existing methods of manufacture of thick and thin film resistors are often not capable of producing values of resistance within the tolerance band required. As a result the initial resistance is normally made about 50 per cent of the final value and the resistor is trimmed by removal of the film material while continuously monitoring the resistance. Discrete resistances and the performance of hybrid circuits can be adjusted in this way, the latter being known as a functional trimming.

Abrasive jets and r.f. discharges are both used to trim both thick and thin films. More recently lasers have been used for trimming thick and thin film components.[90,91,92] Examples of trimming techniques possible with lasers enabling fine and coarse adjustment of resistance to be obtained are illustrated in Fig. 5.29. Various

136

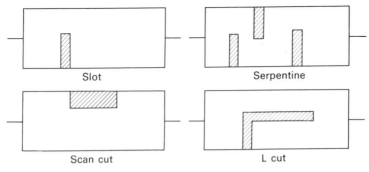

Fig. 5.29 *Methods used for trimming thick and thin film resistors*

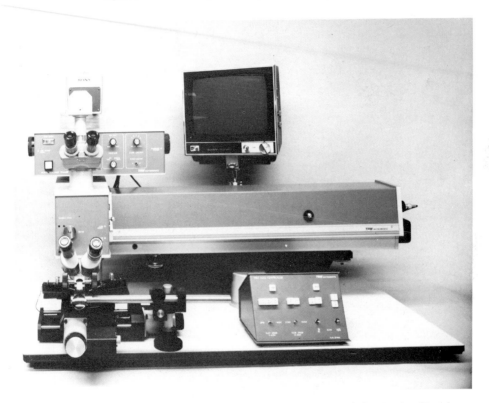

Fig. 5.30 *Xenon laser trimmer using 300 W peak power laser pulsed at 200 pulses/s for trimming thin and some thick film resistors (courtesy Quantrad Corp.)*

systems of varying degrees of complexity using argon, xenon, neodymium, and CO_2 lasers are commercially available. Continuous monitoring of the value of the component with feedback enabling entirely automatic operation is possible and very high throughputs can be achieved. A laser trimming system using a pulsed xenon laser with closed circuit television and motorized two axis control is shown in Fig. 5.30. Sealing of the trimmed edges by glazing, which improves stability, more precise control, reduced contamination, and no wear (for example, of air jet nozzles) are some of the advantages that have been claimed over other methods. Other advantages claimed are cost savings of at least 50 per cent and throughputs six times those of abrasive trimmers.

Moderate power levels are required for trimming applications, typically of the order of 10 W (CW) or 0·01 J/pulse for thick films and 3 W (CW) or 150 W peak for thin films. The high absorption of most metals and low absorption of the non-metal substrate at 1·06 μm make the neodymium-doped laser materials the most obvious choice, although both argon-ion and CO_2 lasers have also been used. Pulsed operation is normally used to minimize thermal damage to the substrate since CW operation can cause excessive melting rather than vaporization. Continuous pumping with a Q-switched output enables relatively low pumping powers to be used resulting in long discharge tube life and tungsten halogen lamps with an acousto-optic Q switch enabling high repetitive peak powers to be obtained have been used[91] suitable for trimming both thick and thin films.

Thick film resistors can be trimmed by vaporization of the resistance film at the edge or centre, or an L-shaped cut can be made.[91] (Fig. 5.29.) Thick film resistors can be trimmed to an accuracy of within 0·3 per cent, cut widths of between 10 μm and 100 μm can be readily made at speeds in excess of 30 mm/s and coarse and fine adjustment can be easily obtained, but non-uniform power dissipation in the resistance film which can cause overheating should be avoided. An automatic system for trimming thick film resistors is shown in Plate VII.

Thin film resistors can be trimmed with laser beams by vaporization or in the case of some cermets by annealing.[92] Energy may be transmitted through an encapsulating medium, enabling otherwise inaccessible parts to be machined and preventing oxidization, if the encapsulating medium is transparent to the laser radiation.[90] Thin film Nichrome resistors have been trimmed to within 0·01 per cent, and low tolerance conventional resistors have also been trimmed in this way. Encapsulated thin film crystal oscillators have been accurately tuned by controlled evaporation of the crystal material. Capacitors have also been produced by scribing a narrow slit in the conducting surface of a thin film, the dielectric being formed by the substrate.[90]

Another application is for the isolation of faulty components in a large integrated circuit by disconnection of conducting paths by evaporation with a laser. Such a process can be built into the testing programme.

5.3.3 Production of masks for integrated circuits

The application of lasers to the manufacture of the masks required for production of micro-circuits has been widely investigated to improve accuracy and overcome the limited life of the mask which is placed in contact with the circuit. Lasers have been used to produce the masks by evaporation of thin film using the output at 1·15 μm of pulsed helium–neon lasers, and CO_2 lasers.[93] The subsequent reduction in size is reduced from 1/120 for conventional graphical methods to about 1/12, enabling improved accuracy and definition to be achieved.

Direct exposure of photoresist material with an argon-ion laser using holographic techniques has been investigated.[94, 95] As well as the high accuracy obtainable, the large depth of focus of holograms enables non-contact masking to be used, resulting in indefinite mask life and higher definition.

A metal sublimation technique in which an image is formed by deposition from a

An unusual application is the use of a pulsed ruby laser as a non-contact remote non-destructive method of measuring corrosion of mild steel bolts used in atomic reactors. The corroded material is vaporized with the ruby laser while a second helium–neon laser monitors the reflectivity which increases by a factor of three to four when the uncorroded substrate is reached, enabling a measure of the depth of the corrosion to be made from the number of pulses to within 20 μm.

5.6 Pollution detection

Light is scattered by gas molecules at different wavelengths by internal lattice vibrations and rotation of the molecules (Raman effect) or Doppler broadened infrared absorption at slightly different wavelengths (Rayleigh scattering). The availability of high-intensity monochromatic light of low divergence from lasers enables spectroscopic analysis by scattering methods to be greatly extended. The availability of laser sources with a monochromatic output of relatively high power in the infrared region where lattice vibrations occur has given added impetus to Raman spectroscopy.[130]

One use receiving considerable attention at present is for remote pollution detection and measurement[131,132] only made practical by the monochromatic low divergence and high intensity obtainable with lasers. The various methods that have been used include Raman scattering, resonance band scattering, and absorption.

Raman scattering utilizes the shift in the wavelength of scattered light corresponding to the characteristic frequency of the molecules. A single-wavelength laser can be used over the transparent spectral region of the atmosphere. A short wavelength is preferred because of the higher energy available since the scattered radiation is small. Argon ion and nitrogen lasers have been used for remote measurements over long distances. The transmitter and detector can be mounted close together. Techniques using back-scattered light are similar to those used for range-finding (LIDAR). (See section 5.1.3).

The absorption of water vapour and carbon dioxide and sulphur dioxide molecules can be detected in a polluted atmosphere with a Q-switched ruby laser and a portable system for monitoring the water vapour emitted by an electrical power station has been developed.[131] A collimated pulse from a ruby laser is directed at the source and the back-scattered signal is collected by a Newtonian telescope and detected by a photo-multiplier. The detected signal gives an indication of the density of the vapour. By tuning the output to the wavelength of absorption of water around 0·6943 μm and comparing the intensity of the back-scattered light outside this band the concentration of water vapour in clouds and haze can be determined. The complete system is shown in Plate IX.

Resonance band scattering due to the characteristic resonance of the molecule can be used to detect and measure pollution concentration. Detection levels of 1 part in 10^6 can be easily achieved. The laser output is tuned to the appropriate resonant wavelength. Parametric oscillators and dye lasers have been used to obtain variable wavelength output. The laser and detector can be mounted adjacent to each other.

Resonance absorption measures the total absorption over the path length without depth resolution. A remote detector or retro-reflector is required. Lower laser power and simpler optics than those required for back-scattering processes can be used. Absorption spectra of almost all known pollutants lies in the region 3–15 μm including

Plate IX LIDAR system in use measuring water vapour emission from a power station (courtesy Central Electricity Research Laboratory)

ozone, sulphur dioxide, ammonia, nitric oxide, nitrogen dioxide, carbon monoxide, and various hydrocarbons. Available laser outputs at high power in the infrared are principally over the region 5–6 µm and 9–14 µm. For low concentrations high energy densities are required. Low nitric oxide concentrations of 1 part in 10^9 have been measured. Some of the overlapping absorption lines of nitric oxide, sulphur dioxide, and carbon monoxide can be compared with laser lines of carbon monoxide and frequency-doubled carbon dioxide over the range 5–6 µm.[116]

Tunable semiconductor lasers and spin-flip Raman lasers also have outputs in the infrared. Tunable diode lasers of the type $Pb_{(1-x)}Sn_xTe$ in which the output wavelength can be varied over the range 6·5 µm to 32 µm by varying the composition factors, have also been used to measure the concentration of carbon monoxide (4·2 µm), carbon dioxide (5 µm) and unburned hydrocarbons at longer wavelengths in automobile exhausts.[131,133] Over short distances where the divergence is acceptable, light-emitting diodes can also be used for absorption spectroscopy, together with tuned detectors.

5.7 Analytical techniques using lasers

Laser photometers may be used to detect many structural features of materials using light-scattering techniques. Examples are colloidal size, size distribution, dielectric structure, and the surface area measurement of aerosols.[134] Other possible applications include nucleation and condensation phenomena, determination of molecular

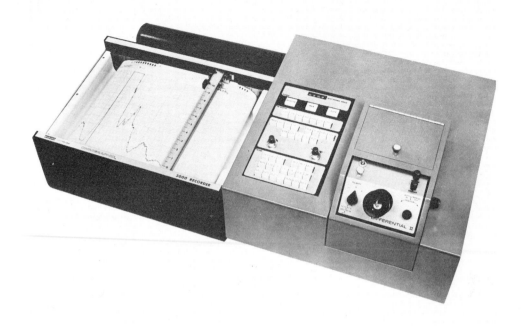

Fig. 5.34 *Differential photometer using an argon ion laser for analysis of single particles (courtesy Science Spectrum Inc., Santa Barbara, Ca.)*

weights, refractive indices, and polymer structures. Macrobiological applications include measurement of cell size and size distribution and wall thickness.

A differential photometer incorporating a single-mode argon ion laser with polarized output is shown in Fig. 5.34. Single particles in the range $0 \cdot 1 \, \mu m$ to $1 \cdot 5 \, \mu m$ diameter are introduced in the laser beam. The detector within the instrument scans the scattered light as a function of angle and the results are used to determine the size, shape, and dielectric structure of the particle. A similar system has been developed for examining particles in solution.

Water droplets and their effects have been studied using a laser as a high-speed pulsed light source with a pulse duration of $2 \cdot 5 \times 10^{-8} \, s$ with a resolution of droplets better than $50 \, \mu m$.[135] The flow patterns in wind tunnels have been studied using the water droplets in saturated air to follow the pressure patterns formed by the model.[136] Lasers have also been used as exploratory tools in combustion processes which have been extensively reviewed.[137]

Turbulence in the entrance of a jet engine has been analysed from the beam spread of a helium–neon laser and compared with scintillation of a CO_2 laser beam.[138] A helium–neon laser has also been used for remote measurements at up to $30 \, m$ of wind velocity using intensity modulation, and Doppler techniques using a $20 \, W \, CO_2$ laser have been used to detect turbulence caused by aircraft at up to $300 \, m$.

A scanning laser microscope has been used for biological examination. The scanning technique using a laser to provide a parallel narrow intense beam enables unwanted reflection to be eliminated so that contrast in a translucent body (e.g., a nerve

149

cell buried in a brain) can be studied with improved definition in this way.[139] In genetics the use of an argon laser is being evaluated as a method of dissecting organic cell structures.

The availability of intense sources in the infrared has opened up new areas of application of Raman spectroscopy[140] (see also 5.6).

A ruby laser spectroscope has been used to analyse small inclusions in metals.[141] The ability to focus laser beams to a very small spot size enables samples as small as 10^{-8} g to be vaporized, so that it is virtually a non-destructive process. A similar technique using a ruby laser together with a microscope has been used to obtain samples of the material condensed on a microscope cover plate for subsequent analysis.[142] A technique using a laser to vaporize a thin film so that direct observation from the opposite side is possible has been described.[143] The method is claimed to simplify viewing optics and allow greater control of the evaporation process.

The temperature distribution in electric arcs has been measured with a laser using the change in refractive index that occurs with temperature.[144] Helium–neon lasers have also been used as an intense monochromatic source of background radiation for examination of welding arcs, enabling the re-radiation from the arc to be selectively filtered out so that the transferring metal droplets in the arc show up against the light background. A similar technique using a ruby laser together with filters has been used to obtain Schlieren photographs of the gas flow in an air blast circuit breaker.[145]

The breakdown mechanism production and interaction of lasers with plasma has been extensively investigated.[146] The very high pulse power outputs obtainable from neodymium and dye lasers has led to speculation about their possibilities as a trigger source for a fusion bomb, and for pulsed thermonuclear reactors.[147] High-power pulsed lasers have also been used to provide high electric fields to operate Kerr cells enabling operating speeds of the order of 10 picoseconds to be obtained[148] and to break down gases[149] and trigger spark gaps.[150–152] For air the electric field at breakdown $E_{max} \approx 3 \times 10^7$ V/m, which can be readily achieved by a high-power focused pulsed laser.

5.8 Applications of holography

A vast amount has been written on the subject of holography. The applications other than purely scientific have been few although considerable interest in potential industrial applications, particularly in non-destructive testing, exists. These are reviewed in detail elsewhere.[153,154] In keeping with the aim of this book, the subject is treated within an industrial rather than scientific context.

A hologram is formed by interference patterns from a spatially and temporally coherent light source. The output of a coherent light source is divided into two beams as shown in Fig. 5.35. One beam is used as a reference beam and directed onto a photographic emulsion, the other is reflected off the object and interferes with the reference beam at the surface of the emulsion. An optical system of high mechanical stability is necessary since a movement of the order of a fraction of a wavelength at the photographic plate during exposure would be sufficient to blur the hologram. Both intensity and phase displacement are recorded in this way in two dimensions from a three-dimensional object. When the hologram is illuminated with a coherent source of the same wavelength and at the same angle as the reference beam during exposure, a

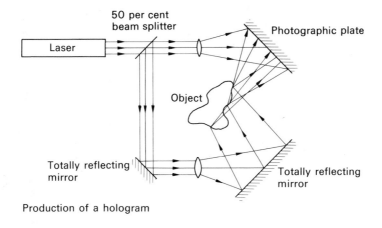

Production of a hologram

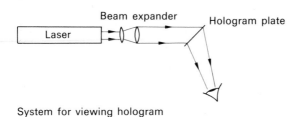

System for viewing hologram

Fig. 5.35 *Production and viewing of a hologram*

three-dimensional image of the object can be seen. The field of view is, however, limited, and for a true three-dimensional effect over a wide range of angles of view a more complex system is required.

The depth of focus is limited by the coherence length of the laser beam used in the exposure of the hologram. When the hologram is viewed by incoherent light it bears no resemblance to the original scene. If a hologram is focused in the normal way but using a lens to localize the holographic image near the recording plate, a hologram is formed which can be viewed with a conventional monochromatic light source, enlarged, and projected.

Some of the properties of holograms are listed in table 5.11.

Holograms of static objects may be produced with CW or pulsed lasers of moderate power level but which are stable to within a fraction of a wavelength during the time of exposure. For this reason pulsed lasers are often preferred.

Ruby lasers are normally used to expose the hologram with subsequent illumination by a helium–neon laser at 0.6328 μm. Argon lasers are also used where high intensity CW illumination is required.

Holographic motion pictures at 20 frames/s have also been recorded. Continuous holographic films can be made of moving objects (as opposed to framed movie pictures) enabling much greater time resolution to be obtained very simply with no 'blind' periods, and also eliminating film wear due to sprocketing and accelerating forces. Holography of moving objects and transient events requires a short pulse of light of high intensity. A hand-held camera incorporating a ruby laser has been developed.[155]

Table 5.11 Some properties of holograms

1. The image formed is three-dimensional yet all the information needed to reconstruct it, both phase and amplitude, can be stored two-dimensionally.
2. Holographic images have enormous depth of field compared with conventional photography, the depth of field being limited only by the coherence distance of the radiation.
3. The normal parallax effect as a viewer moves is apparent in a reconstructed hologram image. An observer can, for example, move as far as the optical arrangement allows in order to see behind something.
4. The hologram itself, unlike a photographic negative, is completely unintelligible when viewed by incoherent light.
5. The hologram image, being produced by the use of coherent illumination, is not pure dark and light tones, but speckled in a fashion reminiscent of a coarse half-tone photograph: this can be a disadvantage if detail is required.
6. Lenses or other conventional image-forming elements are not required in hologram production.
7. The hologram may be enlarged or reduced before reconstruction, but this will change the size and position of the resulting image. Unfortunately the depth of the image is magnified (or de-magnified) more than the height, and so objects will appear distorted, and the quality of the image is also reduced.
8. Holograms can be made of images produced with non-visible light.
9. If a hologram is treated as a photographic negative and used to make a positive on another glass film, the positive will reconstruct the original scene and not a black-white reversal.
10. If a hologram is broken into pieces, each piece can be used to reconstruct the original image, because every point on the subject sends light to every point on the hologram. If the pieces are small, however, the resulting loss in definition can be severe.

The output of neodymium lasers frequency doubled to $0.53\,\mu m$ can also be used. A ruby laser repetitively pulsed at a rate in excess of about twenty pulses per second can also be used to view the hologram. The small difference in wavelength between the radiation used to produce the hologram and the illuminating wavelength is normally insignificant. Q-switching techniques are used to obtain very high power pulses of several joules and of a few nanoseconds duration. Passive dye Q switches enable longitudinal mode selection necessary for a long coherence length. Pockels cells enable accurate synchronization to be obtained; however, separate mode selection, using a Fabry–Perot etalon, is necessary if a coherence depth greater than 100–200 mm is required. Where very high pulse output for very short exposures are required oscillator-amplifier configurations may be used.

Holograms are formed using recording materials normally responding to ultra-violet or visible light. Various films and processing methods suitable for holography are available,[156] such as Kodak emulsion 649F suitable for CW holography and AGFA-Gevaert 10E75 which has been used for Q-switched ruby lasers, and frequency-doubled CW YAG lasers. Holograms have also been produced on photo-resist used for manufacture of integrated circuits.[157]

A variety of applications in engineering processes have been investigated in non-destructive testing including stress analysis, flow detection, and fatigue failure.[158,159] Various techniques of inspection exist including surface distortion in three-dimensions.[160] Double exposure holography, in which the object is photographed, subjected to the stress, and exposed again so that the two wave-forms interfere with each other forming fringing patterns, can be used to indicate the strain and hence the concentration of stress in two and three dimensions. The ability to use holograms to detect very small differences between two apparently identical objects has been used to compare cylinder bores. A contour map of the difference can be obtained from the interference fringes that are formed by superimposing the two holograms.[160] An application of double-exposure holography which has been developed is for the detection of flaws in car tyres[161] which have often escaped X-ray examination. This is done by detection of non-uniformities after heating the tyre slightly or changing the tyre pressure. Internal defects are revealed by changes in the interference contours.

The variation of refractive index of gases with pressure and temperature and the ability to use diffuse reflected light enables conventional interferometer techniques used in wind tunnels, ballistics, and shock propagation studies to be extended to events of shorter duration and to larger structures.

Holography has been used for examination of particle droplet size and distribution in turbine design, fuel nozzles for rockets, and water droplets in jet engine intakes.[162]

Real-time holography uses a hologram formed of the original undeformed object which is developed and the deformed object compared with it. The effect of change in stress can be immediately seen. Gas and air flow patterns and transparent objects can be analysed in this way, enabling the effect of several parameters to be examined.

When a coherent laser beam is reflected from an unpolished surface the reflected beam has a peculiar granular or specked appearance immediately visible to the naked eye.[163] This is known as the speckle pattern and is caused by the constructive and destructive interference at the surface. Speckle pattern techniques can be used to simplify the application of holographic techniques in some applications.[164] The maximum displacement of a vibrating component can be deduced from the nodal areas at which the pattern is brightest. Strain and vibration can be measured in real time without photographic methods using speckle pattern interferometry, already in an advanced stage of development. A speckle pattern interferometer using closed circuit television to display in real time a speckle pattern corresponding to the three-dimensional surface being examined is shown in Fig. 5.36.

The use of holography in microscopy, permitting three-dimensional examination, has been extensively studied.[165] The photographic image obtained from a scanning electron microscope is blurred by diffraction from the finite size of the electron beam and from different electron penetration over the specimen surface. The transparency of the image is illuminated with coherent light from a laser which is passed through a holographic filter and refocused on to photographic film.[166] An increase in magnification of 2, enabling the limit of vision to be extended to $2.5 \times 10^{-4} \, \mu m$, has been achieved in this way. A method of producing a three-dimensional hologram from a sequence of X-ray pictures had also been described.[167]

Probably the most exciting aspect of holography is the high density of information storage that is possible, coupled with the high resistance of the hologram to mal-treatment. This has led to what may be the first major commercial application of holography, for television recording.[168] The high density of information storage possible enables the rapid analysis of large quantities of data with a high degree of security from forgery. One application proposed for holograms is for maps in aircraft where the high information storage coupled with the high degree of immunity to the effect of scratches are advantages. For this reason a very high density of information storage very much greater than by conventional optical methods is obtainable. Other potential areas of application at present being investigated are in computer memories,[169] fingerprint documentation and identification,[170] and credit card validi-

Fig. 5.36 *Video Span Electronic Speckle Pattern Interferometer (courtesy International Research and Development Ltd)*

fication,[171] rail car identification, ideograph storage and translation systems.[172] Computer-generated holograms have also been produced and may find application in graphical display in three dimensions of complex and changing statistical information, particularly where computer processing is already used.

The use of holograms for data processing together with optical computing techniques[173] (as opposed to optical processes in conventional computers) enable high speed sorting and similar processes to be carried out.[174] Optical subtraction techniques between two similar holograms can be achieved by introducing a phase change of 180° between the reference waves used in two different exposures, using the Fourier transform which is relatively insensitive to translational movement, by projecting the image of a transparency of a hologram through a lens by holographic process in which only the difference between two similar records, one of which may be visualized direct in real time, are determined.[174]

Holograms can be used as lenses where the large depth of focus is advantageous.[175] Holograms have also been used as spatial filters without the loss of intensity associated with normal filters and have been used with a ruby laser for micro-machining.[176] A technique using holograms illuminated with a CO_2 laser has been proposed for sequentially printing book pages by fusing heat-sensitive powder.[177] Advantages result from the independence of depth of focus and the high utilization of the total energy compared with other methods of aperturing the beam.

Holographic methods may also be used with ultrasonic waves.[178,179] Since ultrasonic waves can penetrate materials more readily than optical wavelengths, acoustic holography opens up new possibilities in non-destructive testing, particularly where

154

the use of X-rays is unsatisfactory or dangerous. Potential applications also exist in medicine, in particular the examination of the unborn foetus. The lack of suitable recording material for acoustic holography has limited its development up to now, however by immersing the object to be examined in a suitable liquid which is disturbed by the acoustic waves an optical hologram is formed at the liquid surface. The hologram is subsequently illuminated with a laser.

5.9 Communications and information processing

The coherent output and large bandwidth at frequencies in the optical spectrum enable very large amounts of information to be transmitted and their use has been extensively reviewed.[180]

Laser communication systems are limited to line-of-sight applications free from fog, rain, and dust. Effects of temperature variations causing fluctuations in refractive index also limit the range. A system using a helium–neon laser to transmit the signal from a television camera has been developed and is shown in use in Fig. 5.37. The CO_2 laser is promising for high-power transmission over large distances. Atmospheric absorption at $10.6\,\mu m$, principally due to carbon dioxide and water vapour, is relatively low. Its use up to now has been limited by the scarcity of detectors available for use at this wavelength. The feasibility of using lasers together with optical waveguides for inter-city communications is being actively investigated although at present the attenuation of optical waveguides is high.

Fig. 5.37 *Laser communication system. The output of the television camera (left) is used to modulate the output of the helium–neon laser transmitter (right) which transmits the television picture to police headquarters about a mile away (courtesy Optical Communications Inc.)*

A portable short-range communication system using a gallium arsenide laser has been developed for use for military applications and for ship-to-ship communication during refuelling and may also find application for line-of-sight communication on large engineering projects.[181] Some advantages are avoidance of unwanted interception, independence of interference from or with other transmissions, and independence of the influence of earthed or magnetic structures.

Laser systems using CO_2 lasers for space–earth communication requiring precision tracking and pointing systems are being developed.[182,183] The use of CO_2 and Nd:YAG at $1.06\,\mu m$ and frequency doubled at $0.53\,\mu m$ has been reviewed.[180] Potential advantages are the very high communication rates obtainable from compact light-weight systems. The short wavelengths are also capable of transmission through the shield of ionized gas that envelopes space vehicles on re-entry.

Several possible applications of lasers in computers have been proposed. One potential application is for high-speed information transmission within the computer itself, at present limited by the speed at which pulses can be transmitted along wires, which is slow compared with the velocity of light. Transmission rates of 10^9 bits a second are achievable where each bit is a separate piece of information.[184] Data links using fibre optics enable problems associated with transmission within noisy environments such as aircraft and missiles to be eliminated. Another application of lasers in computers is for high-density information storage using the laser as a contactless source for an optically or thermally activated holographic storage medium. A variety of methods using holographic techniques to store information have been studied. By storing the holograms in crystals of lithium niobate or barium sodium niobate at controlled temperatures and subsequently cooling the crystal, ions in the material take up a configuration that is not erased when subsequently illuminated by a reading beam from a laser. Potential storage densities using this technique of 10^{12} bits in a one-centimetre cube are theoretically possible.[185] Optical computers using optical pattern recognition by comparing holograms are also being investigated.

Permanent computer stores capable of up to 10^{12} bits are now commercially available using plastic coated metal film. Data is stored by burning holes in the metal film. with a high intensity laser beam a hole corresponding to a binary one and the absence of a hole a zero. The data is read back using the laser beam at a lower intensity. Very high storage densities are obtainable.

Three-dimensional colour television using three lasers, and large area-displays where high light intensities are required, has been developed. Television recording such as the RCA Selectavision system which uses holograms recorded on tape and reconstructed with a laser is being developed.[168] The use of holograms is claimed to render the tape relatively impervious to rough treatment.

5.10 Other applications

Stimulated germination of seeds has occurred when they have been exposed to the output of a helium–neon laser and the growth of plants has been modified.[186] There is some evidence that plant growth is stimulated and increased yields are obtained in the same way as by mechanically splitting the casing. A possible area of application of lasers is to kill choking underwater vegetation by interfering with enzyme production of bottom-rooted plants without harming fish.

Remote measurement of current at high voltages used for power transmission (which at present requires large and costly current transformers due to the large amount of insulation required) is possible. Several methods using lasers have been proposed using a helium–neon laser directed by fibre optics at a magneto-optic (Faraday effect) quartz or flint glass block on the power line. The angle of deflection of the reflected beam, which is a function of the current in the line, is measured[187,188] (Fig. 5.38).

At present still in the development stage, it is likely to find wide application particularly as transmission voltages rise.

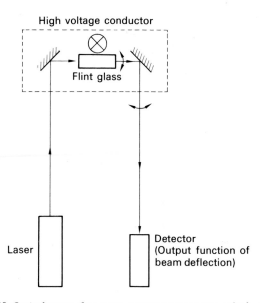

Fig. 5.38 *Optical system for remote current measurement at high voltage*

Identification methods using the monochromatic low-divergence output of lasers have been developed. A technique using a laser for rapid scanning of a reflecting matrix on vehicles using coded rectro-reflective tape has been described[189] and is potentially suitable for such applications as rail car identification, identification of large fleets of transport vehicles and mail bags. The reflected light can be recorded or transmitted through a central processor. One existing application at a knitwear factory concerns the identification of labels of packages and maintenance of inventories by reading bar-coded labels. A similar system using a helium–neon laser and a code of dark and light bars is in use for identifying tobacco kegs and automatically directing them to their correct stations. Advantages claimed over conventional light sources are that no reflective coating is required, the increased depth of field, and the system is not affected by crooked labels.

Velocity of speeding cars is being measured using lasers in America.[190] The method which relies on the interception of two beams 50 mm apart is claimed to be advantageous where conventional radar techniques are not suitable, such as in winding streets and hilly residential areas.

A laser as a lighthouse source is in use in Australia and is particularly suitable for use in low-lying regions because of the small beam divergence and hence effectiveness at low height. Tests are in progress in the UK using two 50 mW helium–neon lasers mounted in a 2·1 m high tower. A rotating optical system also diverges the beam so that at 30 km it is 60 m high and 6 m wide. The output wavelength at 0·6328 μm has better penetration of the atmosphere than conventional beams.[191]

Military applications of lasers in addition to surveillance and range-finding (see section 5.13) include gunnery simulators using pulsed gallium arsenide lasers with suitable detectors mounted on the target.[192] The possibility of the use of lasers to damage critical areas of aircraft or missiles is being investigated. Lasers are also being used as 'target illuminators' for precision location of targets, and missiles have been guided by laser beams.

Intrusion- and fire-detection is possible using the almost parallel beam of monochromatic light from a laser. For intrusion detection the beam is directed at a detector which actuates an alarm when the beam is interrupted. The low divergence of the laser allows long perimeters to be monitored. The use of wavelengths outside the visible region enables the intruder to be detected without his knowledge. CW or pulsed low-power semiconductor lasers with output in the infrared are suitable. The fire detector uses a helium–neon laser to detect smoke by the variation in attenuation of the beam and heat by variation in refractive index resulting in deflection of the beam.[193] A typical system is shown in Fig. 5.39, using a reflected beam to minimize effects due to different path lengths from the source of heat or smoke. Effects due to normal deflection of the building can be overcome by using a multiple detector array.

Printing and recording applications using lasers have been developed together with scanning techniques. A high speed non-impact printer using a helium–neon laser with accousto-optic deflector is shown in Fig. 5.40. A laser writing system has been demonstrated using a laser to transfer ink from a carrier substrate to the surface of the paper on which it is required using an argon ion laser. Several methods using lasers have also been proposed in the patent literature for copying processes. Other applications include high-speed printing processes suitable for the output of computers. The use of a CO_2 laser for drying inks after printing has been patented. An argon laser has been installed instead of a Xenon flash system in a photocomposing machine and is claimed to result in a saving of materials and labour costs. An application of a 200 mW argon laser is to produce a modulable light source for the production of 'paint by numbers' plans from colour photographs.

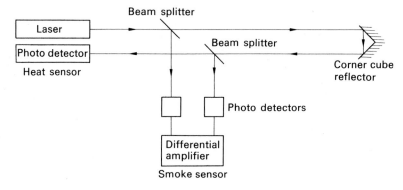

Fig. 5.39 *Optical system for laser smoke and fire detection*

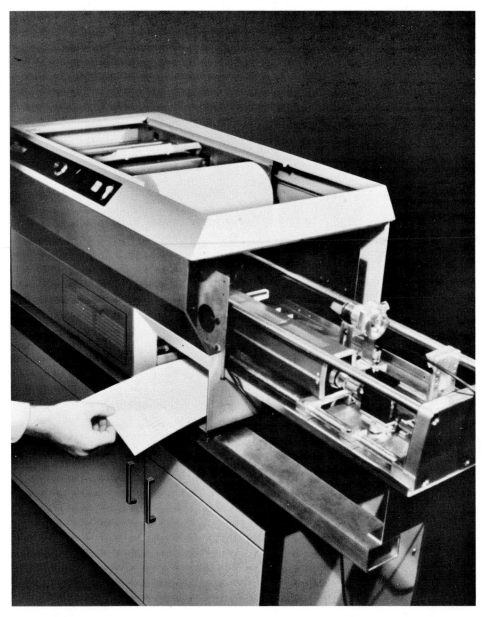

Fig. 5.40 *Non-impact printer using acousto-optic laser deflector capable of output of 5000 lines per minute. The helium–neon laser is shown partly withdrawn in centre with acousto-optic deflector mounted in the end (courtesy Zenith Radio Corporation)*

References

1. Rowley, W. R. C. and Wilson, D. C., 'Design Tolerances in Laser Measurement Systems', *Proc. Inst. Mech. Engrs*, **183** (3D), 29–33, 1968–69.
2. Harris, C. J., 'A Laser Interferometer for Accurate Calibration of Machine Tools', *Mach. & Prod. Engng*, **119**, 96–97, 1971.
3. Tipton, H., 'Laser Measuring Techniques in Machine-tool Applications', *Proc. Inst. Mech. Engrs*, **183** (3), 1–4, 1968–69.
4. 'Laser Beam Speeds Machine Tool Testing', *Metal Working Production*, **115** (3), 45, 1971.
5. Schede, R. W., 'Interferometers for Use as Integral Parts of Machine Tools', *IEEE Ind. Gen. Appl.*, **3** (4), 328–332, 1967.
6. Cooper, B. K., 'Laser Optics – an Invisible Check on Workshop Accuracy', *The Engineer*, **229** (5943/4), 25–27, 1969.
7. Radford, A. F., 'Lasers – A Tool for New Inspection Techniques', *The Quality Engineer*, **34** (2), 2–6, 1970.
8. Bennet, S. J., 'Lasers Metrology and Standards', *Phys. Bull.*, **22** (7), 397–398, 1971.
9. Carson, R. W., 'Laser Measures Diameter of Moving Strand of Wire', *Product Engineering*, **39** (14), 50–52, 1968.
10. West, P., 'Automatic Non-Contacting Measurement of Fine Filaments', *Research*, **4** (1), 6–8, 1971.
11. Binks, S. D., 'The Development of a Laser-Operated Scanning Rod Gauge', *Measurement and Control*, **4** (4), T49–T53, 1971.
12. 'Laser Beam Simplifies Submarine Pipeline Laying', *Pipes and Pipelines International*, **15** (9), 29, 1970.
13. Worth, D. A., 'How Far and How Straight', *Industrial Research*, **11** (8), 13–14, 1969.
14. 'Laser Guidance for Road Laying', *Electronics and Power*, **17** (7), 282, 1971.
15. Skutley, K., 'Precision Alignment Systems', *Civil Engng (ASCE)*, **37** (9), 44–46, 1967.
16. Billman, K. W., Leonard, E. T. and Yaffee, M. A., 'True Vertical Laser', *Appl. Opt.*, **10** (2), 422–425, 1971.
17. Peckham, L. N., Hagler, M. O., and Kristiansen, M., 'Industrial Applications of Lasers', *ISA Trans.*, **9** (3), 216–221, 1970.
18. 'Laser Helps Reactor Building', *Electrical Times*, **158** (19), 53, 1970.
19. 'Laser Puts Axles on Straight and Narrow', *Mach. Des.*, **43** (29), 98, 1971.
20. Wall, M. R., 'Underwater Laser Applications', *Opt. Tech.*, **1** (3), 130–139, 1969.
21. Immarco, A. and Oigardon, T., 'The Pulsed Laser Goes Underwater', *Opt. Spectra*, **4** (8), 34–40, 1970.
22. Hyde, D. J. and Vaughan, P. A., 'Laser Altimeter', *Marconi Instrum.*, **12** (3), 42–44, 1969.
23. Bolgiano, D. R. and Meeks, E. D., 'A Laser Cane for the Blind', *IEEE J. Quantum Electron.*, **3** (6), 44, 1967.
24. 'Three Year Saga of the Laser Cane: Design Improves as Trials Continue', *Laser Focus*, **8** (3), 21, 1972.
25. Becklake, E. J., 'Laser Radar Techniques for the Investigation of the Upper Atmosphere; a Review', *J. Brit. Interplanetary Soc.*, **24**, 33–44, 1971.
26. Botcherby, S. C. L. and Bartley-Denniss, G. A., 'Length and Velocity Measurement by Laser', *Opt. Tech.*, **1** (2), 85–88, 1969.
27. Bourke, P. J. and Brown, C. G., 'Remote Measurement of Mean Wind Velocity and Turbulence by Laser Anemometry', *Optics and Laser Tech.*, **3** (1), 23–25, 1971.
28. Foreman, J. W., George, E. W., Jetton, J. L., Lewis, R. D., Thornton, J. R. and Watson, H. J., 'Fluid Flow Measurements with a Laser Doppler Velocimeter', *IEEE J. Quantum Electron.*, **2** (8), 260–266, 1968.
29. Dennison, E. B. and Stevenson, W. H., 'Oscillatory Flow Measurement with a Directionally Sensitive Laser Velocimeter', *Rev. Sci. Inst.*, **41** (10), 1475–1478, 1970.

30. Kulczyk, W. K. and Davis, Q. V., 'Laser doppler instrument for measurement of vibration of moving turbine blades', *Proc. IEE*, **120** (9), 1017–1023, 1973.
31. Smith, R. C. and Watkins, L. S., 'Ring Lasers and Applications', *Proc. Inst. Mech. Engrs*, **183** (3D), 38–42, 1968–69.
32. 'Laser Gyro Will Continuously Check San Francisco Area's Transit System', *Laser Focus*, **8** (11), 30–31, 1972.
33. Chun, M. K. and Rose, K., 'Interaction of High-Intensity Laser Beams with Metals', *J. Appl. Phys.*, **41** (2), 614–620, 1970.
34. Asmus, J. F. and Baker, F. S., 'Nonlinear Surface Phenomena Associated with Laser Beam Penetration of Metals', *IEEE 10th Symposium on Electron, Ion and Laser Beam Technology*, pp. 241–246 (Ed. L. Marton), San Francisco Press, 1969.
35. Scott, B. F. and Hodget, D. L., 'Pulsed Solid-State Lasers for Engineering Fabrication Processes', *Proc. Inst. Mech. Engrs*, **183** (3D), 75–84, 1968–69.
36. Ready, J. F., 'Effects Due to Absorption of Laser Radiation', *J. Appl. Phys.*, **36** (2), 462–68, 1965.
37. Paek, U. and Gagliano, F. P., 'Thermal Analysis of Laser Drilling Processes', *IEEE J. Quantum Electron.*, **8** (2), 112–119, 1972.
38. Gonsalves, J. N. and Duley, W. W., 'Interaction of CO_2 Laser Radiation with Solids, 1 Drilling of Thin Metallic Sheets', *Can. J. Phys.*, **49** (13), 1708–1713, 1971.
39. Longfellow, J., 'High Speed Drilling in Alumina Substrates with a CO_2 Laser', *Am. Ceram. Soc. Bull.*, **50** (3), 251–253, 1971.
40. Scrase, T. E., 'NC Drilling With The Laser', *Metalwork Prod.*, **114** (2), 60–61, 1970; 'New Laser Developments', *Wel. & Met. Fab.*, **39** (7), 268–270, 1971.
41. 'Speed is the Secret in Drilling Superalloys', *Metal. Prog.*, **98** (2), 10, 1970.
42. Moorhead, A. J., 'Laser Welding and Drilling Applications', *Weld. J.*, **50** (2), 97–106, 1971.
43. Barber, R. B. and Linn, D. L., 'Some Novel Approaches in the Utilization of Lasers in Materials Processing', *IEEE 10th Symp. on Electron, Ion and Laser Beam Technology*, pp. 225–230 (Ed. L. Marton), San Francisco Press, 1969.
44. 'Dual-Beam Laser Technique Makes Clock More Accurate', *Opt. Spectra*, **4** (8), 31, 1970.
45. Hush, I., 'Diamond Dies and Fine Wire', *Industrial Diamond Review*, 12–17, Jan. 1971.
46. 'Lasers, Newest Plastics Fabrication Tool', *Mod. Plast.*, **46** (5), 71–74, 1969.
47. 'Laser Outdoes Needle', *Laser Focus*, **4** (15), 16, 1968.
48. Longfellow, J., 'Production of an Extensible Matrix by Laser Drilling', *Rev. Sci. Inst.*, **41** (10), 1485–1486, 1970.
49. 'CO_2 Beam Perforates Baby Bottle Nipples', *Electrotechnology*, **84** (1), 46, 1969.
50. 'Improvements Relating to Cutting Processes Employing a Laser', Brit. Pat. 1 235 653, 1971.
51. Adams, M. J., 'Introduction to Gas Jet Laser Cutting', *Met. Constr. & Br. Weld. J.*, **2** (1), 1–8, 1970.
52. Lunau, F. W., Paine, E. W., Richardson, M. and Wijetunge, M. D. S. P., 'High-Power Laser Cutting Using a Gas Jet', *Opt. Tech.*, **1** (5), 255–258, 1969.
53. Harry, J. E. and Lunau, F. W., 'Electrothermal Cutting Processes Using a CO_2 Laser', *IEEE Trans Industry Applications*, **8** (4), 418–424, 1972.
54. Lunau, F. W., 'Laser Gas Jet Cutting', *Proc. Conf. on Advances in Welding Processes*, pp. 20–23, Welding Institute, Harrogate, 1970.
55. *Laser Focus*, **8** (4), 14, 1972.
56. McMillin, C. W. and Harry, J. E., 'Laser Machining of Southern Pine', *Forest Products J.*, **21** (10), 35–37, 1971.
57. Doxey, B. C., 'Line-Following Laser System for Cutting Die Board', *Boxboard Containers*, **78** (1), 50–55, 1970.
58. Lunau, F. W. and Doxey, B. C., 'The Laser Cutting of Steel Rule Dies', *Proc. of the 2nd International Conference on Product Development and Manufacturing Technology, 1971*, MacDonald, London, 1973.

59. 'Laser Die-Cutting for the Folding Carton Industry', *Paperboard Packaging*, Part I, **55** (3), 29–31, 1970; Part II, **55** (5), 38–41, 1970.

60. Miller, C. H. and Osial, T. A., 'Status Report on 250 Watt CO_2 Laser for Applications in the Pulp and Paper Industry', *Fifteenth Annual IEEE Pulp and Paper Conference, Atlanta, Georgia, May 1969*.

61. 'Fabricating Plastics with the Laser', *Plast. Design Processing*, **10** (3), 20–23, 1970.

62. 'Take Another Look at Lasers', *Plastics World*, **29** (1), 37–39, 1971.

63. Tandler, W. S. W., 'Production Roles for CO_2', *Laser Focus*, **7** (3), 24–7, 1971.

64. Tencza, A. D. and Angelo, R. W., 'Selective Removal of Teflon Insulation from Wire Using CO_2 and Argon Lasers', *IEEE 10th Symposium on Electron, Ion and Laser Beam Technology* (Ed. L. Marton), San Francisco Press, 1969.

65. Gibbon, J. E., 'Laser Technology', *Hosiery Trade Journal*, **74** (883), 84–85; 88, 1967.

66. Special Issue: 'Laser Cutting – Its Future Potentials', *The Journal of the Apparel Research Foundation*, **5** (1), 1–40, 1969.

67. 'Another Genesco Garment Plant Will Expand its Laser Cutting', *Laser Focus*, **8** (6), 23–24, 1972.

68. Pamphlet AVCO HPL-10 Industrial Laser, AVCO-Everett Research Laboratory.

69. 'Carbon Dioxide Laser Scribes Ceramics at 10ft/min', *Mat. Engng*, **70** (7), 44–45, 1969.

70. 'Clean Fracture', *Mech. Engng*, **90** (7), 57, 1968.

71. 'Laser Materials Processing Enters New Domain: Controlled Fracturing', *Laser Focus*, **4** (9), 12–13, 1968.

72. Pfitzer, E. K. and Turner, R., 'Quartz Working with a CO_2 Laser', *J. Phys. E.*, **1**, 360, 1968.

73. Nelson, L. S., 'CO_2 Laser Enhances Study of Materials', *Ceramic Age*, **86** (11), 38–39, 1970.

74. Cockayne, B. and Gasson, D. B., 'The Machining of Oxides Using Gas Lasers', *J. Mat. Sci.*, **6**, 126–129, 1971.

75. Adams, M. J., 'Gas Jet Laser Cutting', *Proc. Conf. on Advances in Welding Processes*, pp. 142–146, Welding Institute, Harrogate, 1970.

76. Adams, M. J., 'Oxy-Laser Cutting of Metals – Cutting Mechanism', *Weld. Inst. Bull.*, **11** (2), 41–45, 1970.

77. Flinchbaugh, D. E. and Barnard, G. M., 'Metal Machining with an Argon Laser Beam', *16th Symposium on Electron Ion and Laser Beam Technology* (Ed. L. Marton), *IEEE*, San Francisco Press, 1969.

78. Stovell, J. E. and Scott, B. F., 'CO_2 Laser Machining', *IEE Conference on Electrical Methods of Machining and Forming*, London, 1970.

79. Banas, C. M., Walch, A. P. and Brown, C. O., 'Materials Processing with Carbon-Dioxide Lasers', *Electron Ion Laser Beam Technology Conference*, Boulder, Colorado, 1971.

80. *Background Information from AVCO Everett Research Laboratory about the HPL-10 High Power Industrial Laser*, AVCO Everett Research Laboratory.

81. 'Multi-fold Laser Cutting', *Weld. and Met. Fab.*, **40** (1), 32–33, 1972.

82. Fairbanks, R. H. and Adams, C. M., 'Laser Beam Fusion Welding', *Weld. J.*, **43** (3), 97s–102s, 1964.

83. 'CO_2 Laser Welding Joins the Parade', *Weld. Eng.*, **55** (8), 42–44, 1970.

84. Alwang, W. G., Cavanaugh, L. A. and Sammartino, E., 'Continuous Butt Welding Using a Carbon Dioxide Laser', *Weld. J.*, **48** (3), 110s–115s, 1969.

85. Conti, R. J., 'Carbon Dioxide Laser Welding', *Weld. J.*, **48** (10), 800–806, 1969.

86. Houldcroft, P. T., 'The Laser as a Production Tool', *Engng Prod.*, **1** (4), 249–250, 1970.

87. Locke, E. V., Hoag, E. D. and Hella, R. A., 'Deep Penetration Welding with High-Power CO_2 Laser', *IEEE J. Quantum Electron.*, **8** (2), 132–135, 1972.

88. Brown, C. O. and Banas, C. M., 'Deep Penetration Laser Welding', *Am. Weld. Soc. 52nd Annual Meeting*, San Francisco, 1971.

89. Verdu, J. and Chatain, M. 'Le Soudage de Films par Faisceau Laser', *Plast. Mod. Elastomer*, **22** (4), 281–297, 1970.

90. Cohen, M. I., Unger, B. A. and Milkosky, J. F., 'Laser Machining of Thin Films and Integrated Circuits', *Bell. Syst. Tech. J.*, **47** (3), 385–405, 1968.

91. Davies, M. B., Willis, J. B. and Wright, J. K., 'The Use of Lasers for Resistor Trimming', *Int. Soc. for Hybrid Microelectronics Conf. on Adjustment, Assembly and Packaging for Hybrid Microelectronic Circuits*, April 1971.

92. Braun, L. and Breuer, D. R., 'Laser Adjustable Resistors for Precision Monolithic Circuits', *Solid State Tech.*, **12** (5), 56–62, 1969.

93. Rowe, T. J. and Moule, D. J., 'Laser Machining of Photolithographic Masks in Thin Metallic Films', *Proc. I. Mech. E.*, **183** (3D), 13–18, 1968–69.

94. Beesley, M. J., Foster, H. and Hambleton, K. G., 'Holographic Projection of Microcircuit Patterns', *SERL Tech., J.*, **18** (1), 31–32, 1968.

95. 'Masking by Hologram', *Electronics*, **43** (6), 64–5, 1970.

96. 'Laser Speeds Automatic Testing of IC Masks', *Electronics*, **44** (2), 11, 1971.

97. Gupta, D. C., Sherman, B., Jungbluth, E. D. and Black, J. F., 'Non-Destructive Semiconductor Testing Using Scanned Laser Techniques', *Solid State Technol.*, **14** (3), 44–50, 1971.

98. Cohen, M. I. and Epperson, J. P., 'Application of Lasers to Microelectronic Fabrication', in *Electron Beam and Laser Beam Technology* (Eds. L. Marton, A. B. El-Kareh), pp. 139–186, Academic Press, New York, 1968.

99. Nickols, K. G., 'Review of Laser Microwelding and Micromachining', *Proc. IEE*, **116** (12), 2093–2100, 1969.

100. 'Smallest Production Laser Weld must last over 20 Years', *Mat. Engng*, **98** (2), 10, 1970.

101. Hass, G. and Ramsey, J. B., 'Vacuum Deposition of Dielectric and Semiconductor Films by a CO_2 Laser', *Appl. Opt.*, **8** (6), 1115–18, 1969.

102. Ban, V. S. and Kramer, D. A., 'Thin Films of Semiconductors and Dielectrics Produced by Laser Evaporation', *J. Mat. Sci.*, **5** (11), 978–82, 1970.

103. Madani, N. and Nichols, K. G., 'The Use of a Carbon-Dioxide Laser for the Deposition of MOS Diodes', *Israel J. Techn.*, **9** (3), 245–8, 1971.

104. Goldman, L., *Biomedical Aspects of the Laser*, Springer-Verlag, New York, 1967.

105. Goldman, L. and Rockwell, R. J., *Lasers in Medicine*, Gordon & Breach, London, 1972.

106. Hill, D. W. and Powell, T., *3. Application of Laser to Medicine*, Ed. B. W. Watson, IEE Medical Electronics Monographs (1–6), Peter Peregrinus, London, 1971.

107. Goodwin, D. W., 'Lasers in Biomedicine', *Phys. Bull.*, **22**, 407–411, 1971.

108. Wolbarsht, M. L. (Ed.), *Laser Applications in Medicine and Biology*, Vol. 1, Plenum Press/Consultants Bureau, New York, 1971.

109. Polanyi, T. G., Bredemeier, H. C. and Davis, T. W., 'A CO_2 Laser for Surgical Research', *Med. & Biol. Engng*, **8** (6), 541–548, 1970.

110. L'Esperarance, F. A., 'An Ophthalmic Argon Laser Photocoagulation System; Design, Construction, and Laboratory Investigations', *Tr. Am. Ophth. Soc.*, **66**, 827–904, 1968.

111. Beach, A. D., 'Laser Surgery', *AWRE News*, **17** (7), 15–16; 32, 1970.

112. 'Fiber Arm Makes a Laser Scalpel Easy for a Surgeon to Weld and Sterilize', *Laser Focus*, **8** (3), 20–21, 1972.

113. Smart, D. 'Ophthalmic Laser', *Encyclopaedic Dictionary of Physics*, Supplementary Vol. 3 (Ed. J. Thewlis), Pergamon Press, Oxford, 1971.

114. Manson, N., Smart, D. and Ingram, H. V., 'Laser Ophthalmoscope and Coherent Light', *Brit. J. Ophth.*, **52** (6), 441–449, 1968.

115. Smart, D. and Hornby, P., 'The Role of Lasers in Biology and Medicine', *Phys. Bull.*, **20**, 5–9, 1969.

116. Millirio, J., 'Lasers and the Eye', *Ann. Occupational Hygiene*, **10** (3), 31–41, 1967.

117. 'Clinicians find Laser Useful against More Eye Disorders', *JAMA*, **215** (1), 29–31, 1971.

118. Green, D. G., 'Testing the Vision of Cataract Patients by Means of Laser-Generated Interference Fringes', *Science*, **168** (3936), 1240–1242, 1970.

119. Hall, R. R., Beach, A. D., Buter, E. and Morrison, P. C. A., 'Incision of Tissue by Carbon Dioxide Laser', *Nature Lond.*, **236** (5306), 131–132, 1971.

120. Goodale, R. L., Okada, A., Gonzales, R., Borner, J. W., Edlich, R. F. and Wangensteen, O. H., 'Rapid Endoscopic Control of Bleeding Gastric Erosions by Laser Radiation', *Arch. Surg.*, **101** (2), 211–214, 1970.

121. Stellar, S., Polanyi, T. G. and Bredemeier, H. C., 'Experimental Studies with the Carbon Dioxide Laser as a Neurosurgical Instrument', *Med. & Biol. Engng*, **8** (6), 549–558, 1970.

122. Rich, J., 'The Biological Effects of Intense Light', *Ann. Occupational Hygiene*, **10** (3), 13–22, 1967.

123. 'Investigations of the Internal Structure of an Animal Body', Brit. Pat. 1202861, 1970.

124. 'Laser Blasts Tooth Decay', *New Sci. and Sci. J.*, **51** (769), 629–630, 1971.

125. 'Dental and Surgical Applications Widen as Legislation is Debated', *Laser Focus*, **8** (11), 20–22, 1972.

126. Spalding, I. J., 'Laser Systems Development', *Phys. Bull.*, **22**, 401–402, 1971.

127. Dye, M. S., 'Laser Inspection of Image-Orthicon Field Meshes', *J. Sci. & Tech.*, **37** (4), 186–190, 1970.

128. Butters, J. N. and Denby, D., 'Some Practical Uses of Laser Beam Photography in Engineering', *Phot. Sci.*, **18** (6), 60–67, 1970.

129. 'Finding Flaws in Surfaces', *Laser Focus*, **8** (11), 14, 1972.

130. Heavens, O. S., 'Lasers in Scattering Experiments', *Phys. Bull.*, **22**, 385–387, 1971.

131. Altman, L., 'Optoelectronics Engineers Pit Lasers Against Pollution', Parts 1–3, *Electronics*, **44**, 64–68, December 1971.

132. Menzies, R. T., 'Use of CO and CO_2 Lasers to Detect Pollutants in the Atmosphere', *Appl. Opt.*, **10** (7), 1532–1538, 1970.

133. Hinkley, E. D. and Kelley, P. D., 'Detection of Air Pollutants with Tunable Diode Lasers', *Science*, **171** (3972), 635–639, 1971.

134. 'Exploiting Lasers', *Electrical Times*, **154**, 644, 1968.

135. Proctor, T. D., 'A Laser Technique for the Measurement of Aerosols', *J. Phys. E.*, **1**, 631–635, 1968.

136. Walters, S., 'The Laser in Aerospace', *Mech. Engng*, **93** (5), 43–44, 1971.

137. Schwar, M. J. R. and Weinberg, F. J., 'Laser Techniques in Combustion Research', *Combustion & Flame*, **13**, 335–374, 1969.

138. Hogge, A. and Visinsky, W. L., 'Laser Beam Probing of Jet Exhaust Turbulence', *Appl. Opt.*, **10** (4), 889–892, 1971.

139. Davidovits, P. and Egger, M. D., 'Scanning Laser Microscope for Biological Investigations', *Appl. Opt.*, **10** (7), 1615–1619, 1971.

140. Loader, J., *Basic Laser Raman Spectroscopy*, Heyden-Sadtler, London, 1970.

141. Ryan, J. R. and Cunningham, J. L., 'Laser Microprobe Helps Identify Inclusions', *Metal Progress*, **90** (6), 100–103, 1966.

142. Adams, M. D., 'Ultramicrosampling with a Laser', *Microscope*, **19** (2), 157–169, 1971.

143. Mela, M. J. and Sulonen, M. S., 'A New Method of Laser Microprobe Analysis', *J. Phys. E.*, **3**, 901–903, 1970.

144. 'Temperature Measurement with Laser Light', *Sheet Metal Industries*, **48** (2), 159, 1971.

145. 'What Really Happens in a Circuit-Breaker', *Elec. Times*, **153**, 176, 1960.

146. Schwarz, J. (Ed.), *Laser Interaction and Related Plasma Phenomena*, Plenum Press/Consultants Bureau, New York, 1971.

147. 'Dye Lasers to Trigger H-Bombs', *New Sci.*, **44** (627), 460, 1969.

148. Basov, N. and Krokhin, O., 'Laser Light for Fusion Fire', *New Sci. & Sci. J.*, **51** (771), 733–734, 1971.
149. Smith, D. C., 'Gas Breakdown with 10·6μ-Wavelength CO_2 Laser Radiation', *J. Appl. Phys.*, **41** (11), 4501–4505, 1970.
150. Alcock, A. J., Richardson, M. C. and Leopold, K., 'A Simple Laser Triggered Spark Gap with Subnanosecond Risetime', *Rev. Sci. Inst.*, **41** (7), 1028–1029, 1970.
151. Wilson, J. R., 'Laser-Induced Multiple Breakdown in Gases', *J. Phys. D.*, **3**, 2005–2008, 1970.
152. Ujihara, K. and Kamiyama, M. 'Triggering of Spark Gaps by Laser-Induced Ion Emission', *IEEE J. Quantum Electron.*, **6** (4), 239–241, 1970.
153. Caulfield, H. J. and Lu, S., *The Applications of Holography*, Wiley-Interscience, New York, 1970.
154. Robertson, E. R. and Harvey, J. M. (Eds.), *The Engineering Uses of Holography*, Cambridge University Press, Cambridge, 1970.
155. 'Hand-held Laser Camera for Industry', *Electronics and Power*, **17**, 381, 1971.
156. Pennington, K. S., 'Holographic Parameters and Recording', *Handbook of Lasers* (Ed. R. J. Pressley), Chemical and Rubber Publishing Co., Ohio, 1971.
157. Beasley, M. J. and Castledine, J. G., 'The Use of Photoresist as a Holographic Recording Medium', *Appl. Opt.*, **9** (12), 2720–2724, 1970.
158. Burchett, O. J. and Irwin, J. L., 'Using Laser Holography for Non-Destructive Testing', *Mech. Engng*, **93** (3), 27–33, 1971.
159. Burch, J. M., 'Holography in Non-Destructive Testing', *Phys. Bull.*, **20**, 501–502, 1969.
160. Archbold, E., Burch, J. M. and Ennos, A. E., 'The Application of Holography to the Comparison of Cylinder Bores', *J. Sci. Inst.*, **44** (7), 489–494, 1967.
161. 'Austrian Tiremaker's Holograms', *Laser Focus*, **8** (6), 20, 1972.
162. Beatson, C., 'Beaming in on the "fringe benefits" of Holography', *The Engineer*, **231** (5993), 36–37, 1970.
163. Archbold, E., Burch, J. M., Ennos, A. E. and Taylor, P. A., 'Visual Observation of Surface Vibration Nodal Patterns', *Nature Lond.*, **222** (5190), 263–265, 1969.
164. Butlers, J. N. and Leendertz, J. A., 'Speckle Pattern and Holographic Techniques in Engineering Metrology', *Optics & Laser Technology*, **3** (1), 26–30, 1971.
165. Cox, M. E., 'Holographic Microscope – a Review', *Microscope*, **19** (2), 137–150, 1971.
166. Stroke, G. W., 'Sharpening Images by Holography', *New Sci. & Sci. J.*, **51** (770), 671–674, 1971.
167. Redman, J. D., 'Three-Dimensional X-Ray Pictures', *Atom* (167), 186–191, 1970.
168. '"Pressing" Pictures on Holographic Tape is Fast, Inexpensive', *Electronics*, **42** (23), 108–113, 1969.
169. 'Laser Memories – Distant Pipeline or Imminent Revolution?', *New Sci. & Sci. J.*, **51** (759), 80, 1971.
170. 'Optical-memory terminals reappear for use with credit and ID cards', *Laser Focus*, **8** (8), 15, 17, 1972.
171. 'For Identification, Flash your Hologram', *Electronics*, **43** (21), 52, 1970.
172. Heagerty, L., 'Ideaographic Composing Machine', *Appl. Opt.*, **9** (10), 2291–2294, 1970.
173. Khol, R., 'Optical Computers', *Mac. Des.*, **41** (9), 116–124, 1969.
174. Bromley, K., Monahan, M. A., Bryant, J. F. and Thompson, B. J., 'Holographic Subtraction', *Appl. Opt.*, **10** (1), 174–181, 1971.
175. Kock, W. E., Rosen, L. and Rendeiro, J., 'Holograms and Zone Plates', *Proc. IEEE*, **54** (11), 1599–1601, 1966.
176. Moran, J. M., 'Laser Machining with a Holographic Lens', *Appl. Opt.*, **10** (2), 412–415, 1971.
177. 'Printing a Book at a Time by Laser Holography', *New Sci.*, **41** (637), 402, 1969.
178. Metherell, A. E., 'Acoustical Holography', *Sci. Am.*, **221** (4), 36–44, 1969.
179. Korpel, A., 'Acoustic Imaging and Holography', *IEEE Spectrum*, **5** (10), 45–52, 1968.

165

180. Special Issue on Optical Communications, *Proc. IEEE*, **58** (10), 1970.
181. 'Portable Optical Communicator Rides Laser for Secure Voice Transmissions', *Electronics*, **43** (6), 92–96, 1970.
182. Goodwin, F. E., 'A Review of Operational Laser Communication Systems,' *Proc. IEEE*, **58** (10), 1746–1752, 1970.
183. Forster, D. C., Goodwin, F. E. and Bridges, W. B., 'Wide Band Laser Communications in Space', *IEEE J. Quantum Electron.*, **8** (2), 263–272, 1972.
184. 'New Laser Circuits Carry Billion Bits a Second', *Opt. Spect.*, **4** (11), 11–12, 1970.
185. 'Permanent Storage for Holographic Images', *Electronics and Power*, **17**, 380, 1971.
186. Paleg, L. G. and Aspinall, D., 'Field Control of Plant Growth and Development through the Laser Activation of Phytochrome', *Nature Lond.*, **228**, 970–973, 1970.
187. Saito, S., Fujii, Y., Yoloyama, K., Hamasaki, J. and Ohno, Y., 'The Laser Current Transformer for EHV Power Transmission Lines', *IEEE J. Quantum Electron.*, **2** (8), 255–259, 1966.
188. Rogers, A. J., 'Optical Techniques for Measurement of Current at High Voltage', *Proc. IEE*, **120** (2), 261–267, 1973.
189. 'Laser Beam Scans Mini-Labels on Packages', *Mod. Materials Handling*, **25** (3), 50–52, 1970.
190. 'Two Laser Beams Clock Speeders for Police', *Mac. Des.*, **43** (12), 8, 1971.
191. 'Laser Lighthouse', *Electron Technology*, **84** (1), 43, 1969.
192. Paton, J. O. G., 'Tank Crew Training with Simfire', *International Defense Review*, **4** (5), 442–444, 1971.
193. 'A Laser Fire Detector', *Design Electronics*, **8** (10), 15, 1971.
194. Thompson, B. J., 'Application of Lasers to Printing and Recording', *Image Tech.*, **11** (10), 16–24, 1969.

6

SAFETY

The hazards from lasers vary with the wavelength, intensity, and duration of the output or length of exposure and it is difficult to generalize. However, operating procedures and precautions can be specified over the various ranges of outputs of available lasers.

Radiation from lasers is non-ionizing and essentially optical in nature with relatively shallow penetration, unlike microwave or nuclear radiation. Lasers present potential safety hazards but can usually be guarded against with a few simple precautions. The principal hazard is normally to the eyes, although body burns may also occur at high powers.

The high voltage power supplies normally required, toxic fume production, cryogenic equipment, and vacuum implosion may also present hazards; however, these hazards are more widely understood and are not dealt with here.

6.1 Transmission and absorption of the eye

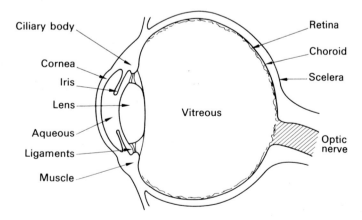

Fig. 6.1 *The construction of the eye*

The individual elements of the eye are shown in Fig. 6.1. The incident ray is focused first by the cornea; fine focus is achieved with the lens. The iris acts as a variable aperture whose opening varies with the intensity of the light falling on it. The incident ray is focused onto the retina surface which comprises a pigmented layer (the epithelium) and the choroid.

The transmission characteristics of the eye have been extensively investigated. The transmission characteristics of the part of the eye which is transparent to visible radiation are shown in Fig. 6.2.[1] Beyond about 1·3 μm the transmittance of this region is approximately that of a layer of pure water 22 mm thick. Over the visible region part of the incident radiation is absorbed, scattered, and reflected, the remainder being transmitted to the retina. The percentage reflectivity is relatively small except in the region around 1·1 μm at which it is around 50 per cent of the incident radiation.

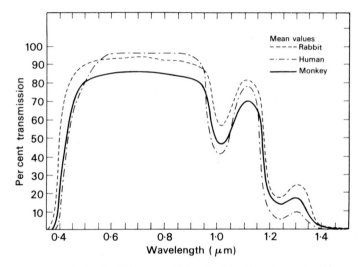

Fig. 6.2 *Percentage transmission for light of equal intensity through ocular media of human, monkey, and rabbit eyes (from Geeraets, W. J. and Berry, E. R., 'Ocular Spectral Characteristics as Related to Hazards from Lasers and Other Light Sources', Am. J. Ophthalmology, **66** (1), 15–20, 1968)*

The percentage absorption at the retina and choroid is shown in Fig. 6.3.[1] Comparison of the curve for the transmission of the front part of the eye and the absorption at the retina and choroid, together with the visibility characteristic of the eye (Fig. 6.4)[2] indicates that the eye is capable of efficiently transmitting wavelengths beyond the visible region (approximately 0·4 μm to 0·8 μm) in the near infrared. This is potentially as dangerous as visible light although it is not possible consciously to focus it on the retina.

In the visible region the cornea is able to focus light, including indirect reflections, on the retina. This is shown in Fig. 6.5(a). Incident light at the cornea with a beam diameter of up to 7 mm governed by the aperture of the pupil may be focused to a spot close to a diffraction limited spot size of around 10 μm diameter corresponding to an increase in energy density at the retina over that at the cornea of about 5×10^5. On this basis a beam of incident energy of 0·05 mW/mm² at the cornea becomes 25 W/mm² at the retina. Light outside the visible region in the near infrared can still be uncon-

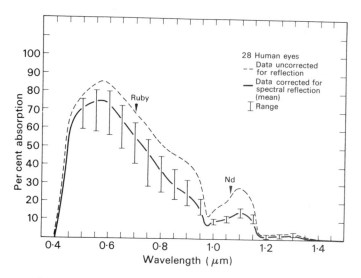

Fig. 6.3 *Percentage absorption in human retinal pigment epithelium and choroid for equal intensities and light incident on the cornea, R = ruby laser wavelength, Nd = neodymium laser wavelength (from Geeraets, W. J. and Berry, E. R., 'Ocular Spectral Characteristics as Related to Hazards from Lasers and Other Light Sources', Am. J. Opthalmology, 66 (1), 15–20, 1968)*

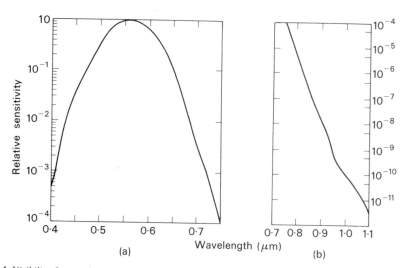

Fig. 6.4 *Visibility factors for the eye:* (a) *relative sensitivity of a standardized normal eye to light of varying wavelengths;* (b) *sensitivity in the near infrared (from Smith, W. J., Modern Optical Engineering, page 111, McGraw-Hill, New York, 1966)*

sciously focused and transmitted by the cornea, although invisible, as shown in Fig. 6.5(b).

Light of wavelengths below about $0.2\,\mu m$ and above about $0.9\,\mu m$ is increasingly absorbed by the cornea and at wavelengths beyond about $1.5\,\mu m$ absorption by the cornea is likely to be almost complete. This condition is illustrated in Fig. 6.5(c).

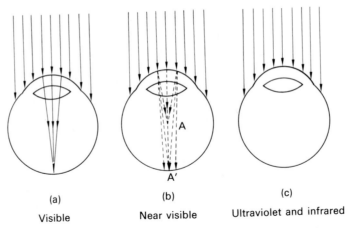

(a)   (b)   (c)

Visible   Near visible   Ultraviolet and infrared

Fig. 6.5 *Effect of wavelength on transmission and absorption of light in the eye*

6.1.1 Effects of exposure to radiation The effect of exposure to high power or prolonged exposure at low power over the region 0·4 μm to 1·4 μm where the front part of the eye is transparent, may be to damage the retina tissue and in particular the pigment epithelium, causing lesions and leading to permanent blindness. Additional damage may also occur due to absorption in the cornea and surrounding areas. Damage to the peripheral area surrounding the retina, which is used for general awareness rather than direct observation, may also occur but escape notice until a systematic eye investigation is carried out.

A significant amount of damage to the retina is immediately apparent to the subject first as a white spot which changes to a black spot after several days. The spot eventually disappears from consciousness but remains as a blind spot and is apparent when looking at a plain white surface. Lesions or other damage to the retina can be observed by dilating the pupil of the eye and examining it under magnification. A photographic record is easily obtained. Recovery from lesions of the retina at very low powers may be possible but repeated exposure is likely to cause permanent damage.

Radiation at both short and long wavelengths which is not transmitted but is absorbed in the cornea and the crystalline lens can cause cataract formation at low powers even though the intensity may be so low as not to cause any sensation. The formation of cataracts or microscopic lesions can be determined by an ophthalmologist using a slit lamp microscope. Photographic records are less easy to obtain due to the transparency to visible radiation of the cornea.

Ultraviolet wavelengths below about 0·32 μm cause photophthalmia. High-pressure discharge lamps with quartz walls, as well as some lasers, radiate ultraviolet light at these wavelengths. Radiation is invisible in this region and the effect is often delayed. The effect is similar to sand in the eye and is due to the surface of the cornea rubbing off and exposing nerve tissue. Low-level indirectly reflected light causes some discomfort not unlike conjunctivitis experienced by welders exposed to ultraviolet light. The cells of the cornea are normally continuously replaced but minor damage may occur even from reflected radiation, though it is visible normally only under a microscope. The damage does not apparently affect the sight. Intense radiation may cause rapid expansion of the liquid media and permanent damage to the cornea.

6.2 Effect on the body

The effect of laser beams on the body has already been discussed in section 5.4.3 dealing with laser surgery. For surgical applications, however, the laser power is confined to only sufficient levels to carry out the surgery. At higher powers damage can be more severe and at very high powers, such as those now available from CO_2 lasers, very harmful or even fatal.

The damage and its extent will depend again on the wavelength which will affect the penetration depth. The spectral transmittance of human tissue from a cheek is shown in Fig. 6.6.[3] Transmission increases in the near infrared at about 1 μm but decreases as the wavelength increases due to the increase in absorption of water. When reflection at the surface is allowed for, a percentage transmission of around 18 per cent at 1 μm occurs and relatively deep burns can be expected at around this wavelength. In the middle infrared and ultraviolet regions where the absorption is high, burns are likely to be confined to the surface. Even exposure to indirect radiation can cause harmful effects at high powers. Shallow laser burns tend normally to heal rapidly with normal treatment without leaving a scar, despite the presence of some carbonization.

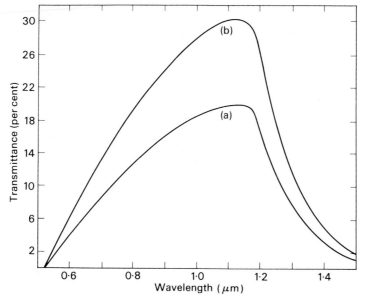

Fig. 6.6 Spectral transmittance curves of human tissue (cheek) 5 mm thick: (a) external transmittance; (b) internal transmittance assuming 34 per cent reflection loss (after Vasko, A., Infra-Red Radiation, Iliffe Books, London, 1968; courtesy SNTL Prague)

The effect of focusing a laser beam is greatly to increase the power density at the focus but after this the beam diverges until at distances greater than the focal length from the lens the intensity is lower than that at the output window of the laser and decreasing with the square of the distance from the focus. An additional hazard in the use of gas jet cutting systems is the increased cutting effectiveness of the beam which results in a deeper cut than would be caused by exposure to the beam alone.

6.3 Threshold levels

The specification of threshold values for the safe observation of lasers in an unconfined environment is by its nature difficult, and a number of different recommended maximum levels of safe exposure exist, which vary over a wide range. Many of these have been summarized together with threshold values for damage from a large number of sources.[4]

Reasons for the wide variation include the varying effects of wavelength, pulse intensity, and duration, and the difficulty of relating experiments on eyes taken from animals and dead human beings to living human eyes. The precise identification of the minimum level of damage is also difficult when the effects of cumulative exposure are not known. The difference between the threshold value and the accepted safety level tends to vary with the standpoints adopted by different organizations, such as the armed forces, where risk of exposure to a single pulse close to the threshold value may be accepted whereas repetitive exposure at the same level in a laboratory may not.

The effect of pulsed lasers is dependent on the intensity and duration of the pulse. For the same energy output the hazards due to Q-switched or mode-locked lasers are generally greater than pulsed outputs at the same energy output.

The damage to animal and human eyes from ruby and neodymium lasers has been extensively studied as a function of pulse energy and duration and the results from a wide variety of sources have recently been summarized.[6] The damage caused by CW helium–neon, argon ion, and CO_2 lasers has been summarized as a function of power and duration of exposure. Safety threshold levels based on many of these results allow between one and two orders of magnitude safety margin for direct exposure or specular reflection.

Safety levels in the United States of America have been proposed by the Committee of the American National Standards Institute (Z-136),[7] the Bureau of Radiological Health, and The American Conference of Government Industrial Hygienists (1973),[8] and various State and Federal standards also exist. Many of the State and Federal codes are mandatory for the laser manufacturer or user or both.

A code of practice recommended by the British Standards Institution (BS 4803:1972)[5] gives maximum safe exposure levels and is summarized in tables 6.1 and 6.2.

Maximum permissible values of exposure based on damage to the retina derived from measurements of damage over the visible region,[6] are given in table 6.1. The corresponding maximum permissible exposure levels at the cornea in table 6.2 are derived from table 6.1 by multiplying the values by 5×10^5 based on a relaxed eye over the visible range. Where a series of repetitive pulses are used the peak pulse energy and the continuous energy levels should not be exceeded.

An additional restriction for CW lasers, and in particular helium–neon lasers, is where self-mode-locking results in high peak powers which may not be indicated by power meters intended for CW use.

The threshold values in tables 6.1 and 6.2 can be related to other wavelengths over the region in which the eye is transparent using the graph of the variation of absorption at the retina with wavelength (Fig. 6.3) assuming 100 per cent instant energy reaches the retina at the wavelength corresponding to the peak sensitivity of the eye at $0.56\,\mu m$. The threshold values obtained for the ruby laser should, however, not be relaxed by more than an order of magnitude in this region.

Table 6.1 *Retinal maximum permissible exposure levels for laser radiation – direct illumination or specular reflection (from BS 4803:1972 Protection of Personnel Against Hazards from Laser Radiation. Reprinted by permission of the British Standards Institution, 2 Park Street, London W1A 2BS)*

Laser Type	Energy Density Per Pulse		Power Density
	Q-Switched 1 ns–1 µs Pulsed p.r.f < 10 Hz	Long Pulsed 1 µs–0·1 s p.r.f < 10 Hz	Continuous Wave Long-Term Exposure (See Notes)
	J/m^2	J/m^2	W/m^2
Ruby (0·69 µm)	$1·6 \times 10^2$	$5·2 \times 10^3$	$1·8 \times 10^3$
Neodymium (1·06 µm)	$9·4 \times 10^2$	$1·5 \times 10^4$	$1·0 \times 10^4$
Helium-neon (0·63 µm)	—	—	$1·5 \times 10^3$
Argon (0·51 µm) (0·48 µm)	—	—	$1·5 \times 10^3$

Table 6.2 *Corneal maximum permissible exposure levels for laser radiation – direct illumination or specular reflection (7 mm pupil) (from BS 4803:1972 Protection of Personnel Against Hazards from Laser Radiation. Reprinted by permission of the British Standards Institution, 2 Park Street, London W1A 2BS)*

Laser Type	Energy Density Per Pulse		Power Density
	Q-Switched 1 ns–1 µs Pulsed p.r.f < 10 Hz	Long Pulsed 1 µs–0·1 s p.r.f. < 10 Hz	Continuous Wave Long-Term Exposure (See Notes)
	J/m^2	J/m^2	W/m^2
Ruby (0·69 µm)	3×10^{-4}	1×10^{-2}	4×10^{-3}
Neodymium (1·06 µm)	2×10^{-3}	3×10^{-2}	2×10^{-2}
Helium-neon (0·63 µm)	—	—	3×10^{-3}
Argon (0·51 µm) (0·48 µm)	—	—	3×10^{-3}

NOTE 1. 'Long-term' exposure relates to work such as holography, where viewing can take place for several hours a day over many days.
NOTE 2. With CW lasers (but not for mode-locked lasers), for any single exposure the limit may be relaxed for occasional (e.g., accidental) exposure to $1·25$ W/m^2 at the pupil.

In practice direct exposure under near field conditions to the beam or its specular reflection of any laser is likely to be above the safety threshold and should be assumed to be potentially hazardous unless shown to the contrary.

An important relaxation of threshold values is accepted in BS 4803 for CW lasers, in particular the helium–neon laser whose outputs are in the visible region, for occasional accidental exposure of $1·25$ W/m^2 at the pupil. The relaxation on the exposure level is based on the instinctive movement of the eye which occurs when exposed to a bright source. Such accidental exposure might occur when using a helium–neon laser for alignment or surveying for example. (The beam diameter of a helium–neon laser with an output of 1 mW at a power density of $1\cdot25$ W/m^2 is 32 mm which can be readily achieved with a collimator and is suitable for many applications.)

Below about $0\cdot4\,\mu$m and above about $1\cdot4\,\mu$m damage to the cornea is the principal hazard. Since focusing at the retina does not take place the threshold levels can be considerably relaxed; however, little available data exists on threshold values outside the visible region. Outside the visible light region below a wavelength of about $0\cdot4\,\mu$m the safe exposure level recommended by BS 4803 should not exceed 130 J/m^2 per day, or $2\cdot16$ W/m^2 for 1 minute, or a correspondingly higher density over a shorter period. At infrared wavelengths above about $1\cdot4\,\mu$m the maximum intensity from a single pulse should be limited to 1 kJ/m^2 and for continuous exposure the average level should be limited to 500 W/m^2.

Maximum exposure levels at the skin, excluding the eye, are taken as the same for all lasers at 1 kJ/m^2 for a single pulse and 1 kW/m^2 for continuous exposure.

The ANSI Z136 Standard[7] gives maximum permissible exposure (MPE) levels for different lasers and modes of operation. The MPE is based on power intensities corresponding to a factor of 10 less than the level at which a 50 per cent probability of causing occular damage exists.

The ANSI Standard is very comprehensive, covering the entire optical spectrum, and anticipates almost every possible contingency, including MPE levels for the eyes and body, for direct and indirect exposure, for various pulse and exposure durations including single pulse, repetitively pulsed, and cw operation. The MPE are generally higher than those proposed by BSS:4803, except for pulses of short duration.

The lasers are classified in five different categories based on the hazards involved depending on the wavelength and power (CW or pulsed) of the laser output. The categories are as follows:

1) Low power, exempt from control measures or medical surveillance.
2) Low power control measures applicable. Medical surveillance not required (CW visible region only).
3) Medium power. Control measures and medical surveillance required.
4) High power. Control measures and medical surveillance required.
5) Totally enclosed systems. Control measures required.

The control measures and medical surveillance required in each category are specified and include details of symptoms of over exposure to laser radiation.

The ANSI Standard also recognizes a special case of CW visible lasers, with CW output powers of less than 5 mW and where the power density is less than 25 W/m^2, which fall into Class 3; these are required only to display the warning 'do not view laser beams with optical instruments'.

The threshold limit values (TLV) proposed by the American Conference of Governmental Industrial Hygienists[8] are similar and in many cases the same as those proposed in ANSI Z136. They are, however, less comprehensive, but include most conditions likely to be encountered at present.

From an industrial users viewpoint, almost all lasers likely to be encountered, with the exception of low power CW lasers in the visible region (notably the helium neon laser), exceed the maximum recommended threshold levels of BSS:4803 and fall into

Class 3 or Class 4 in ANSI Z136. These are normally operated in industrial environments in totally enclosed systems corresponding to Class 5 operation.

6.4 Eye protection

Where risk of exposure to laser outputs above the threshold values exists optical protection must be worn. The likelihood of accidental exposure should wherever possible be minimized by enclosing the laser beam and confining staff to safe areas. Eye protection, while a desirable precaution, should only be regarded as a last line of defence. Optical protection should be regarded as being ineffective for direct exposure to high power CW or pulsed lasers and should be used as protection only against scattered and reflected radiation.

A substantial measure of protection against indirect exposure to the laser beam can be obtained by suitable filters mounted in goggles or glasses. Goggles are inherently safer as no unprotected region exists before the eyes, but are often uncomfortable when worn over a long period and are therefore unsuitable for continuous use. The use of glasses with suitable side-pieces to prevent stray radiation entering at the sides is often more comfortable and easier to enforce.

Various proprietary filters for optical protection for various lasers are available. At long wavelengths in the infrared (above about 5 μm) and wavelengths below about 0·2 μm the attenuation of glass and Perspex is such that they may be used for protection against stray radiation. Toughened glass or a plastic–glass laminate is desirable to minimize damage if the glass is suddenly shattered mechanically or by direct exposure to high-intensity radiation.

For protection in the visible region a narrow band stop filter with a high reflectivity at the appropriate wavelength is most suitable as only a small reduction in overall visibility results. Narrow band pass filters are used to assist beam location by scattered light from low-power helium–neon lasers but do not provide any optical protection.

Where more than one type of laser is in use, requiring glasses with different filters, it is essential that the glasses should be clearly identified.

6.5 Precautionary measures

It is essential that everybody concerned with the operation or use of lasers under conditions of Class 3 or 4 should have a knowledge of their potential hazards and the safety procedures involved. A safety officer should be appointed, who should be responsible for records and safety procedures, and for liaising with the medical authorities undertaking surveillance. The safety officer should ideally be one of the operating personnel because of the highly specialist nature of the hazards involved, and work in collaboration with other safety officers.

It is important that personnel concerned with lasers should be given a full eye inspection by a clinical ophthalmologist before taking up their duties, at periodic intervals, if any accidental exposure is known to have occurred, and on terminating those duties. Details of the specialized eye examinations required have been summarized[7,9] and should initially include a microscopic examination of the cornea and a photographic record of the retina for future reference should be obtained.

The degree of precautionary measures varies with the type of laser, power output

Table 6.3 *Common conditions of laser usage*

Application	Normal Operating Conditions and Precautions
Laboratory use (research, development, and maintenance, etc., above threshold value)	Open path, restricted technical personnel; optical protection mandatory. Visible and/or aural warning required for pulsed lasers
High-power industrial applications (fabrication processes, etc., above threshold value)	Totally enclosed system with interlocks
Low-power industrial applications (surveying, interferometers, etc., below threshold value)	Avoid looking at beam or its reflection directly
High-power (range-finders, communications, pollution detection, etc., above threshold value)	Open path, restricted access requiring special precautions

(CW or continuous operation), and whether it is used in an enclosed area. A convenient category of laser usage is given in table 6.3 although this should only be regarded as a guide.

The obvious precautionary measure is to avoid exposure of personnel to radiation at all times by totally enclosing the beam. This is relatively easily accomplished when the laser is part of a complete system such as those used in scribing or diamond drilling. Although the power density of a focused laser beam may be high at the focus it decreases as the square of the distance from the focus. As a result it is possible to manufacture enclosed laser systems out of a combination of normal materials such as aluminium and asbestos which have either a high reflectivity or absorb at the laser wavelength provided the distance from the focus is adequate. Indirect viewing of the working zone is possible using optical filters which do not transmit at the laser wavelength. In many cases closed circuit television is used giving complete isolation and enabling strain-free magnified view of the operating zone to be obtained. At $10 \cdot 6 \, \mu m$ windows of acrylic sheet can be used provided they are of adequate thickness.

Operation with a totally enclosed system is not always feasible when adjusting a system or carrying out experimental work. A special case is the use in surveying of low-power lasers such as the helium–neon laser below about 2 mW which has already been discussed in section 6.1. Even then elementary precautions ensuring that staff do not look directly into the beam should be taken.

Where operation of an unenclosed or partly closed system (e.g. during maintenance) takes place, the region in which the laser is being operated should be clearly indicated. This should be as small as consistent with safety and contain only personnel working directly on lasers. In the case of industrial laser installation this is best achieved by initially installing the laser in a separate room. At all entrances to this region a cautionary sign should be displayed. Examples of signs recommended in ANSI Z136 are illustrated in Fig. 6.7. These are based on the red sunburst symbol with the type of laser written above the tail on the sunburst. Special precautions or protective actions required are written below. At the top the appropriate warning 'Caution' for Class 2 and a limited range of Class 3 CW visible lasers ($0 \cdot 4 – 0 \cdot 7 \, \mu m$ with an output power below 5 mW and a maximum emergent beam irradiance of 25 W/m² over a 7 mm aperture). The 'Danger' sign is required for other Class 3 and all Class 4 lasers.

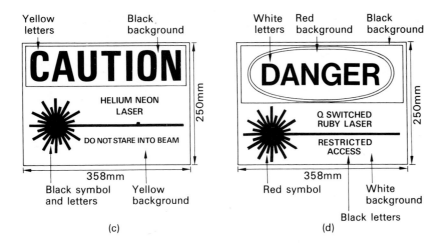

Where lasers are being used in unenclosed systems additional warning, such as a flashing light, visible through the optical protection used is also desirable.

Laser systems with continuous outputs outside the visible region should have indicator lamps clearly visible from all parts of the system. The use of high power pulsed lasers requires special warning devices to be used including audible and visible signals, signals for starting the charging cycle and a count down before firing should be rigorously adhered to. Premature breakdown should be guarded against and accidental firing should be prevented.

The output should be directed into an absorbing enclosure away from other workers. Unwanted energy from high-power pulsed or CW systems can be dissipated (dumped) in various ways. Experimental systems often use refractory brick in which case allowance for diffuse reflection should be made. A preferable system normally employed in high-power industrial systems is the use of a calorimeter which is also used for power measurement.

The general illumination level should be kept high to keep the pupil of the eye constricted at all times so that the effect of accidental exposure is minimized. Specular and diffuse reflections from reflecting surfaces including walls and ceiling should be minimized. Low reflectivity paint may be used bearing in mind the variation in reflectivity with wavelength. (Paints with a low reflectivity in the visible region often have a high reflectivity in the infrared.)

Special sanction should be required for non-laser personnel, maintenance staff, cleaners, etc., to enter the restricted area. At all entrances a supply of suitable glasses or goggles should be provided and during tests mandatory signs requiring all personnel to wear optical protection should be displayed.

A mandatory safety code and operating procedure for use by all personnel working on CO_2 lasers at BOC is shown in table 6.4.

Table 6.4 *Mandatory safety code used at BOC*

1. The Manager in charge of any section where a CO_2 laser is being used shall appoint a Safety Officer, preferably employed in the section and should ensure that he receives adequate safety training.

2. The Safety Officer shall be responsible for:
   2.1. Instituting and maintaining adequate safety methods in line with para 3.
   2.2. Continuing identification of all employees at risk and arranging their safety training.
   2.3. Initiating and updating records.
   2.4. Liaising with site Health Services, informing them of all cases of known accidental exposure.

3. The general precautions to be observed are:
   3.1. The areas in which lasers are used are to be defined and signs stating 'Caution Laser' displayed at all entrances to these areas.
   3.2. Whenever possible all work is to be carried out with the beam totally enclosed. When this is not possible then signs stating 'Laser Test in Progress. No Admittance without Eye Protection' should be displayed by the operator and a red light illuminated at all entrances when the laser is in use. To ensure the effectiveness of this sign it must be displayed only during the period of the test.
   3.3. Where a laser is used, under circumstances other than with the beam totally enclosed, eye protection must be worn by *all* personnel present. The operator will be responsible for checking that an adequate supply of goggles or glasses is available and ensuring that all personnel present wear suitable protection. Anyone ignoring these instructions should be reported to the Safety Officer. When direct access is required to the laser beam, for example when exposing the beam on asbestos sheet, the arms should be covered and gloves worn.
   3.4. Any incident must be reported to the Safety Officer as soon as possible and, if appropriate, reported through the usual channels as an accident.
   3.5. A full eye examination of all personnel who may be exposed to laser radiation is required before taking up such duties, and periodic examination of the eyes, including the cornea, should be carried out every six months thereafter. These examinations should be performed by a specialist ophthalmic surgeon, who should be supplied with a job description for each individual employee, together with details of his known record, and a summary of the known ophthalmic effects of CO_2 laser irradiation. The six-month interval between examinations may be reduced in certain circumstances—for example after known accidental exposure.

References

1. Geeraets, W. J. and Berry, E. R., 'Ocular Spectral Characteristics as Related to Hazards from Lasers and other Light Sources', *Am. J. Opth.*, **66** (1), 15–20, 1968.
2. Smith, W. J., *Modern Optical Engineering*, McGraw-Hill Book Co., New York, 1966.
3. Vasko, A., *Infra-red Radiation*, Iliffe, London, 1968.
4. Clarke, A. M., 'Ocular Hazards', *Handbook of Lasers*, pp. 3–10 (Ed. R. J. Pressley), The Chemical Rubber Co., Ohio, 1971.
5. 'Guide on Protection of Personnel against Hazards from Laser Radiation', BS 4803:1972.
6. Vassiliadis, A., *et al., Investigations of Laser Damage to Ocular Tissues*, Stamford Research Institute Final Report, March 1968. See also Vassilidiadis, A., Zweng, H. C., Peppers, N. A., Peabody, R. R. and Honey, R. C., 'Thresholds of Laser Eye Hazards', *Arch. Environ. Health*, **20**, 161–175, 1970.
7. *American National Standard for the safe use of Lasers*, ANSI Z136, 1–1973, American National Standards, Inc., New York, USA.
8. *Threshold Limit Values for Physical Agents Adopted by ACGIH for 1973, Lasers*, 69–83, American Conference of Governmental Industrial Hygienists, Cincinnati, Ohio, USA.
9. 'Safety with Lasers', *Brit. Med. J.*, **3** (5765), 3–4, 1971.

SELECTED READING LIST

Physical optics

Several general texts are available and include:

Ditchburn, R. W., *Light*, 2nd Edition, Blackie, London, 1963.
Jenkins, F. A. and White, H. E., *Fundamentals of Optics*, 3rd Edition, McGraw-Hill, New York, 1957.
Born, M. and Wolf, E., *Principles of Optics*, Pergamon Press, Oxford, 1970.

Design of optical components and systems

Smith, W. J., *Modern Optical Engineering. The Design of Optical Systems*, McGraw-Hill, New York, 1966.
Kingslake, R. (ed.), *Applied Optics and Optical Engineering*, Volumes 1–4, Academic Press, New York, (1–3) 1965, (4) 1967.

Optical properties of materials

Gray, D. E. (ed.), *American Institute of Physics Handbook*, 3rd Edition, McGraw-Hill, New York, 1972.

Electro-optics

Yariv, A., *Introduction to Optical Electronics*, Holt, Rinehart and Winston, New York, 1971.

Lasers

Lengyel, B. A., *Laser Light*, 2nd Edition, Wiley Interscience, New York, 1971.
Maitland, A. and Dunn, M. H., *Laser Physics*, North Holland Publishing Co., London–Amsterdam, 1970.

Laser applications

Gagliano, F. P., Lumley, R. M. and Watkins, L. S., 'Lasers in Industry', *Proc. IEEE*, **57** (2), 114–147, 1969.
'Lasers and the Mechanical Engineer', *Proc. Inst. Mech. Engrs*, **183**, 3D, 1968–69.

Holography

Caulfield, H. J. and Lu, S., *The Applications of Holography*, Wiley Interscience, New York, 1970.

Safety

Clarke, A. M., 'Ocular Hazards', *Handbook of Lasers*, pp. 3–10 (Ed. R. J. Presley), The Chemical Rubber Co., Ohio, 1971.
'Guide on Protection of Personnel Against Hazards from Laser Radiation', BS 4803: 1972.
American National Standard for the safe use of Lasers, ANSI Z-136 1–1973, American National Standards, New York.

APPENDIX 1
SOURCES OF INFORMATION ON DEVELOPMENTS IN LASERS AND ELECTRO-OPTICS

Periodicals, journals, and abstracting sources dealing exclusively with lasers and electro-optics

Laser Focus (Advanced Technology Publications, Newtonville, Mass.) Monthly.
Laser Sphere (Sphere Inc., Michigan City, Ind.)
The Laser Weekly (Lowry-Cockroft Abstracts, Evanston, Ill.)
The Laser Report (Advanced Technology Publications, Newtonville, Mass.)
Journal of Current Laser Abstracts (Institute for Laser Documentation, Felton, Cal.)
Laser Marketeers and Buyers Guide (Published annually with January edition of *Laser Focus*)
Laser Users Survey (Electronic Industries Association, Washington DC) Annually

Periodicals, journals, and abstracting sources with extensive treatment of lasers

Physics Abstracts (IEE, London, IEEE, New York, AIP, New York)
Electrical and Electronics Abstracts (IEE, London, IEEE, New York, AIP, New York)
Electronics Abstract Journal (Cambridge Communications Corp., Washington D.C.)
IEEE Journal of Quantum Electronics (IEEE, New York)
Optical Spectra (Optical Publishing Co., Pittsfield, Mass.)
Optics and Laser Technology (IPC Science and Technology Press, Guildford)
Electro-optics (Milton Publishing Co., London)
Electro-optical System Design (Milton S. Kiver Publications, Chicago)

APPENDIX 2
GLOSSARY OF LASER TERMINOLOGY

Acousto-optic effect: acoustically generated pressure waves can be used to induce bi-refringence in some transmitting materials. Applications include beam deflection and modulation.

Amplifier: optical cavity without feedback capable of amplification only.

Bandwidth: the range of wavelengths either side of the characteristic wavelength of the output of a laser.

Bi-refringence: naturally or artificially occurring variation in refractive index.

Characteristic wavelength: the wavelength at which the laser output is normally a maximum.

Chemical laser: a laser in which the excitation results from a chemical reaction. *See also* Hybrid laser.

Coherence: used to describe the spatial and temporal relations at different points in a beam of light. The coherence depth is the distance over which the beam remains coherent.

Continuous wave: abbreviated to CW, continuous output.

Crystalline laser: *see* Solid-state laser.

Divergence: characteristic property of light beams resulting in increase in cross sectional area with distance from source.

Dye laser: organic liquid laser optically pumped.

Electron beam pumping: laser (normally gas or semiconductor) in which an electron beam is used to excite the laser transition.

Electro-optic effect: electrostatically induced bi-refringence obtained in some optically transmitting materials. (*See also* Kerr's and Pockels effects.)

Gas laser: laser in which the active medium is a gas, normally excited by an electric discharge.

Gas transport laser: gas laser in which a high gas flow rate occurs across the optic axis of the laser.

Glass laser: solid-state laser which uses glass as the host for the optically active material.

Harmonic generation: use of non-linear optical materials to convert light at one wavelength to other wavelengths which are integral multiples of the original (fundamental wavelength). (*See also* SHG and parametric oscillator.)

Hybrid laser: chemical laser in which the reaction is initiated with an electric discharge.

Infrared: region of the optical spectrum extending from 0·77 μm to 1000 μm.

Injection laser: *see* Semiconductor laser.

Ion laser: laser in which ionization is necessary to cause the laser transition.

Kerr cell: an electro-optic device (*see also* electro-optic effect).

Laser cavity: region bounded by end mirrors and boundaries of laser medium.

Laser head: used to describe the laser as distinct from other associated optical components or power supply.

Lidar: optical radar technique (LIght Detection And Ranging).

Liquid laser: normally used to describe inorganic liquid laser.

Magneto-optic effect: magnetically induced bi-refringence.

Metal vapour laser: similar to a gas laser but the laser action occurs in a metal vapour.

Mode locking: the condition of a fixed phase relation of modes in a laser beam.

Mode structure: spatial relation of intensity distribution transverse to the direction of propagation of the beam.

Modulator: device (normally electro-optic or accousto-optic) for varying phase and intensity of laser output.

Molecular laser: gas laser in which laser action results from molecular transitions. Output is in infrared part of spectrum.

MPE: Maximum Permissible Exposure level (ANSI Z136) based on a factor of 10 below the level at which a 50 per cent probability exists of damage occurring.

Oscillator: term sometimes used for laser cavity.

Oscillator–amplifier: combination of laser cavity together with cavity without feedback.

Parametric conversion: *see* Parametric oscillator.

Parametric oscillator: an electro-optic device used for frequency conversion and tuning by mixing two optical frequencies in a non-linear material to obtain a third which may be the sum or difference of the two input frequencies.

Pockels effect: form of electro-optically induced bi-refringence.

Pulsed output: normally used to describe pulsed outputs other than Q switched or mode locked.

Pumping source: method of exciting laser transition, e.g., flash tubes, gas discharge, etc.

Q Switch: device used to prevent optical feedback from the end mirror in a laser cavity until required so as to obtain high peak power pulse. Sometimes referred to as Q spoiling.

Semiconductor laser: laser in which excitation occurs in a semiconductor normally excited by an electric field.

SHG: second harmonic generation.

Slope efficiency: marginal efficiency above the threshold level.

Solid-state laser: laser in which the active material is a crystalline host.

Spin flip laser: a semiconductor laser whose output wavelength can be tuned with a magnetic field.

TEA laser: acronym for Transverse Excitation at Atmospheric pressure laser.

Threshold level: minimum input power required to obtain laser action.

TLV: Threshold Level Value (ACGIH – 1973) values of exposure to laser radiation under conditions to which nearly all workers may be exposed without adverse effects.

Uni-phase: a term sometimes used to describe a single-mode laser.
YAG laser: Yttrium Aluminium Garnet, one of the hosts used for neodymium-doped
   lasers.

INDEX

Absorption, 25–26, 32
ACGIH, 172, 174
Acoustical holography, 154–155
Acousto-optic:
  effect, 44–46
  materials, 46
Air, absorption, 34–35
Alkali halides, 31–32
Amplification, 8–9
Amplitude, 14–15
ANSI Z136, 172–177
Anti-reflection coating, 25
Aperture, 62
Aspect ratio, 117, 133
Atmospheric absorption, 34–35
Attenuation, 25–26
Attenuators, optical, 62
Axicon lens, 118–119

Beam finders, 103, 175
Beam radius, 14–15
Beam manipulators, 140–142
Beam splitters, 52
Black body radiation, 3–5
Birefringence, 36–38
Bolometer, 64
Brewster angle, 19, 25, 50–51, 72–73
BSS 4803, 172–174, 176
Burns, laser, 171

Cadmium telluride, 32
Calorimeters, 62–65
Cataphoresis, 84

Chromatic aberration, 55
Coherence, 7, 17–18
Collimators, 56–57
Coma, 55

Depth of focus, 113
Detectors, 62–65
Dielectric coatings, 32–34
Diffraction:
  grating, 52, 61
  limited, 15, 53–56, 112
Discharge lamp:
  efficiency, 22, 79
  power supplies, 7
Discharge lamps, continuous, 76–77
Dispersion, 26–27
Divergence: 13–15, 56–57
  half angle, 14
Doppler effect, 108–111
Drilling:
  pulse duration, 117
  re-solidification, 117
Dye cell, 21, 60

Efficiency:
  conversion, 22–23
  slope, 22
Electric mixing laser, 86
Electromagnetic:
  field, 18
  radiation, 1–3
  spectrum, 2
Electro-optic effect, 38–44
Emissivity, 4

Energy:
  output, 20–22
  measurement, 62–65
  transitions, 1–3, 5–7
Etalon, 50
Exothermic cutting process, 125
External transmittance, 24–25
Eye:
  absorption, 167–170
  construction, 167
  effects of exposure, 170
  examination, 175
  protection, 175
  sensitivity, 169

F-number, 53
Fabry-Perot interferometer, 50
Faraday effect, 44, 157
Feedback, optical, 8–9
Fibre optic, 58, 142
Figure of merit, acousto-optic, 46
Filter, spatial, 62
Filters, interference, 33–34
Flash lamps: 73–76
  efficiency, 22–23
Fluorescent, 5–6
Frequency multiplication, 13, 43–44
Fresnel number, 10

Gallium arsenide, 31–32
Gas dynamic laser, 86, 93
Gas jet assistance:
  cutting, 119
  drilling, 115

Gas lasers, 81–87
Gaussian intensity
    distribution, 14–15
Germanium, 31–32
Glasses, 26–31
Glossary, 183–185

Half-wave voltage, 41–42
Heat affected zone, 115, 128
Hole-coupled cavity, 50
Hologram:
    camera, 151
    double exposure, 152–153
    lasers, 151–152
    moving picture, 151
    production, 151–152
    properties, 152
    real time, 153
    recording materials, 152
Holography, 151–155
Hydroxyl ion, 30

Industrial applications:
    analytical techniques:
        absorption of pollutants,
            147
        biological applications,
            149–150
        colloidal size, 148
        combustion processes, 149
        dielectric structure, 148
        differential photometer,
            149
        flow patterns, 149
        particle size distribution,
            148
        spectroscopy, 149
        surface area measure-
            ment, 148
        temperature distribution
            in arcs, 150
        wind velocity measure-
            ment, 150
    communication:
        line of sight, 156
        space communication,
            156
        surveillance, 155
    computing:
        computer memory, 156
        high speed data
            transmission, 156
        optical pattern
            recognition, 156
        three dimensional
            television, 156

Industrial applications (contd):
    cutting:
        acrylic resin, 119
        aircraft industry, 127
        alumina, 124
        carpets, 124
        carton formes, 121–123
        ceramics, 124
        composite materials, 124
        cutting rates, non metals,
            121
        glass, 124
        laser cutting, quartz, 125
        mens suits, 124
        paper, 123
        rates, metals, 126
        scribing, 124, 135–136
        sheet metal, 127
        stainless steel, 126–127
        defects, 153
        finger print identification,
            153
        identification, 154
        lens, 154
        micromachining, 154
        microscopy, 153
        optical computing, 154
        particle sizing, 153
        speckle pattern inter-
            ferometer, 153
        stress analysis, 152–153
        surface distortion, 152
        television recording, 153
        ultrasonic holography,
            internal examination,
            154–155
    length measurement:
        calibration, 98–100
        interferometer, 98–100
        textiles, 124
        thermal fracture, 124
        wood, 119–121
        wood composites, 121
    distance measurement:
        altimeter, 108
        dust layer, 108
        fog, 107
        obstacle detection for
            blind, 108
        underwater, 107
    drilling:
        alumina, 118
        aerosol nozzles, 119
        baby bottle teats, 119
        buttons, 119
        diamond dies, 118

Industrial applications (contd):
        dynamic balancing, 118
        elastomers, 119
        parameters for metals,
            117
        plastics, 119
        spinneret plates, 117
        turbine blades, 117
        watch balance wheels, 118
    electronic component
    manufacture:
        capacitor manufacture,
            138
        evaporation of semi-
            conductor thin films,
            140–141
        insulation removal, 124
        inspection, 139, 145–146
        isolation of faulty
            components, 138
        masks:
            for integrated circuits,
            138
            metal sublimation, 138
            photoresist, 138
        scribing substrates, 135–
            136
        soldering, 140
        testing:
            masks, 139
            shadowgraph, 139
        thermal fracture,
            substates, 124, 136
        trimming crystal
            oscillators, 138
        welding, 140
    holography:
        computer memory, 153,
            156
        credit card validification,
            153–154
        scanning gauge, 101–102
        wire gauge, 101
    medical:
        brain, 145
        cauterization, 144
        dentistry, 145
        photocoagulation, 142–
            143
        skin blemishes, 145
        tumours, 145
        vocal chords, 145
    other applications:
        card speed offence, 157
        corrosion measurement,
            147

Industrial applications (contd):
  fire detection, 158
  germination, 156
  gyroscope, 111
  identification, 157
  intrusion detection, 158
  lighthouse, 157–158
  measurement, dynamic
    pressure, 100
  paper inspection, 145
  plasma formation, 150
  printing and recording,
    158
  remote current measure-
    ment, 157
  spheroidizing, 125
  target location, 158
  thermometer trimming,
    118
  surveying and alignment:
    air frame assemblies, 105
    atomic reactor, 105
    coalmining conveyor, 105
    crane track, 106
    deflection:
      of bridges, 106
      of dams, 106
      of ship deck, 106
    dredging, 103, 105
    level grading, 103
    linear accelerator, 105
    road surfacing, 103
    ships stern tube, 105
    trench digging, 103
    tunnel boring, 103
  velocity measurement:
    extrusions, 110
    fibres, 110
    oscillatory flow, 110
    strip and sheet, 110
    vibration, 111
  welding:
    conduction limited,
      examples, 132
    deep penetration,
      examples, 133
    electronic components,
      140
    quartz, 125
Ion laser, 86–87
  intensity, 14–15
  interference coatings, 32–34
interferometer, 98
Irtran, 32–33
Kanigen, 48
Kerf width, 119

Kerr effect, 39–40
lamp dip effect, 83
Laser cavity, 9
  characteristics, 69
  classification, safety, 174
  disc, 81
  emission, properties, 7
  excitation, 68
  gas, 81–87
  power supplies, gas, 82–83
  operation, 8–9
  properties, summary, 69
  solid state, 71–81
  type, applications, 12
Laser types:
  argon, 86–87
  carbon dioxide, 84–86
  carbon monoxide, 92
  chemical lasers, 93
  dye, 87–89
  erbium, 92
  gallium arsenide, 89–92
  helium cadmium, 84
  helium–neon, 83–84
  inorganic liquid, 92
  krypton, 86–87
  neodymium, 78–81
  nitrogen, 92
  ruby, 78
  selenium hydrogen, 92
  xenon, 92
Lasers, methods of excitation,
  68
Laser usage, safety, 176
Lenses, 52–56
LIDAR, 106–107, 147
Light guide, 58
Liquid laser, inorganic, 92

Magneto-optic effect, 44, 157
Mirrors:
  cavity, 48–51
  coatings, 47–49
  substrates, 50
Mode:
  locking, 21, 60
  selection, 17
  structure, 16–17
Modulation, 39–43
Moiré fringe, 100
Molecular lasers, 93
Mounting, lenses, 55
Mounting, mirrors, 51

Optical materials, properties,
  28–29

Optical subtraction, 154
Oscillator-amplifier, 17, 78

Parametric frequency
  conversion, 43–44
Phase matching, 43–44
Plasma, 114–115
Pockets effects, 39
Polarization, 18–19
Polarizing, prisms, 36–38
Polarized output, 50–51, 72
Polymethyl methacrytale,
  30–31
Population inversion, 6–8
Power densities, typical, 111
Power, output, 20–22
Power measurement, 62–65
Prisms:
  polarizing, 36–38
  reflecting, 51–52
Profile following systems,
  121–124, 133–135
Pseudo welds, 131
Pulse power, 20–22
Pyroelectric detector, 63

Q switches, 21, 59–60
Quadrant detector, 103?
Quartz, 30

Raman effect, 147–148
Rayleigh scattering, 147
Reflection coating, dielectric,
  32–34
Reflection coating, metallic,
  47–49
Reflection loss, 25
Refractive index, 27–29
Resistor trimming, alternative
  methods, 136
Resonator, optical, 9–10
Retardation plate, 38
Retinal damage, 170
Retroreflector, 51–52
Ring laser, 110–111

Safety, 167–179
  code, 178
  procedures, 175–178
  signs, 177
Sapphire, 30
Scanning methods, 65
Scattering, atmospheric, 34–35
Second harmonic generation,
  43–44
Selective emitters, 5

Semi-conductor laser, 89–92
Silica, 29–30
Silicon, 31
Solid state lasers, 77–81
Speckle pattern interferometer, 154
'Spin-flip' laser, 91, 148
Spontaneous emission, 3–6
Stability amplitude, 21–22
Stability, cavity, 9–10
Stability, mode, 16–17
Stimulated emission, 6–7

Thermal runaway, 32

Thin film coatings, 32–34
Threshold level, absorption, 126
Threshold levels, pumping, 172–175
Transmittance, external, 25
Transverse excitation laser, 85–86, 92
Transverse flow laser, 85
Truncation, 62

Velocity of light, 3
Verdets constant, 44

Water, absorption, 35–36

Wavelength:
    characteristic, 13
    output, 11–13
    resolution, 13, 83
    selection, 60–62
Welding:
    alternative processes, 129, 131
    conduction limited, 127–131
    deep penetration, 131–133
Wiens law, 4

X-ray laser, 92–93

Zinc selenide, 31–32